"Come here or I'll come and get you!"

Andreas's dark eyes narrowed as he voiced the threat.

Lauren turned from the window. "What's wrong? Feeling cross again? The nurse says it's a mark of convalescence."

"Come here," he said again, reaching for her. His hand caught hers and he dragged her down onto the bed, holding her so that she could not escape.

"Let me go!" she exclaimed, twisting to avoid his hard mouth as it traveled across her cheek in search of her lips. He jerked her head around and as she glared at him she knew.

"You...remember!" She breathed with a shake in her voice, and her anger flared. "When did you remember?"

"After your second visit to the hospital," he said coolly. She stayed still, incredulous, her face white with shock....

Other titles by

CHARLOTTE LAMB
IN HARLEQUIN PRESENTS

Other titles by

CHARLOTTE LAMB
IN HARLEQUIN ROMANCES

◆

CHARLOTTE LAMB

storm centre

Harlequin Books

TORONTO · LONDON · NEW YORK · AMSTERDAM
SYDNEY · HAMBURG · PARIS · STOCKHOLM ·

Harlequin Presents edition published July 1980
ISBN 0-373-10371-9

Original hardcover edition published in 1980
by Mills & Boon Limited

CHAPTER ONE

THE telephone rang while Lauren was delicately touching in a trace of white among the massed dark clouds in the painting. She hissed with impatience. Of all things she disliked being interrupted at work since it broke her concentration. Sticking the brush between her teeth she walked quickly to the phone, lifted it and asked brusquely, 'Yes?'

'Could I speak to Miss Lauren Grey?' The voice which answered had a faint foreign intonation, a hint of hesitation.

Lauren's face reflected sudden shock and wariness. 'Speaking,' she said, taking the brush from her mouth.

'Lauren?' Her caller sounded even more uncertain.

'Who is it?' There was a husky note to Lauren's voice now, and the hand holding the telephone tightened until her knuckles showed white.

'Lydia,' said the woman, adding quickly, as though afraid Lauren would slam down the phone. 'I had to call you. Andreas....'

'I'm not going to talk about him,' Lauren cut in tersely. 'Now or ever. I've told you that before, Lydia. I don't want to hurt your feelings. I know you mean well, but I have absolutely no interest in your son.'

'You don't understand, Lauren,' Lydia said with a stifled sound which was oddly like a sob.

'I understand very well,' Lauren said coldly, forehead creased. 'Oh, don't cry, Lydia! You mustn't let it upset you. Andreas isn't worth it.'

The sound came again, more deeply. Lauren forgot the brush she held and ran a shaking hand through her hair, streaking it with white paint. 'Lydia, don't cry, for God's sake. I'm sorry.'

'He's dying,' the trembling voice whispered. 'Dying, Lauren.'

For a few seconds Lauren just stood there, staring at the misty grey sky she could see beyond the window. Shock echoed through her system, making her stomach clench, her eyes widen, a chill disbelief rise into her throat.

'What do you mean?' She could barely speak the words, they breathed like a ghostly sigh through her white lips.

'He was driving from Heathrow when he crashed. A lorry had overturned, spilling oil across the road. Andreas didn't see until it was too late. It took them two hours to cut him out of the car.' Lydia stifled another sob. 'He lost so much blood, Lauren. He's so white.'

'Oh, God!' Lauren barely knew she spoke. She was shaking so much she had to lean against the wall or she would have fallen down. All the colour had left her face. The diamond on her hand flashed like a star as her fingers tightened further around the telephone.

'Is he unconscious?' she asked after a moment.

'That's why I'm ringing,' Lydia told her quickly. 'He came round a few moments ago and the first thing he said was your name.'

'Mine?' Lauren closed her eyes.

'He asked where you were, he asked when you were coming.' Lydia was speaking very fast as though still afraid Lauren would hang up. 'Lauren, he still thinks you're his wife.'

The silence stretched between them for a long, long time. Lauren was breathing heavily, a painful incredulity in her eyes.

Then she said thickly, 'Why do you say that?'

'It was obvious,' Lydia told her. 'He said: "Where's Lauren? Where's my wife?" At first I thought he was just dazed, but then after a few minutes I realised what was wrong. Lauren, he has lost his memory. He doesn't remember the divorce, anything that has happened in the last five years. He has forgotten Niko. I mentioned him and Andreas said, "Who?" I was so shocked, so frightened.'

'Was he concussed in the accident?'

'The doctors say so. His head injuries were serious. They operated when he was first brought in and they thought that they had relieved some pressure there was on the brain, but who knows?'

Lauren moistened her lips. 'You ... you said he was dying. Is that what the doctors think?'

'You know what they are like, Lauren. They hedge, they are evasive. But you can see it in their faces, hear it in their voices. They look at one and it is obvious.'

'But what do they say?'

'Oh, that he is not doing too well—that is how they put it. He is very seriously injured, they told me, and just now they said that if you could come it would be advisable.'

'If I could come?' Lauren's eyes widened and the

green became a vivid brilliance against which the white of her skin showed dramatically. She bit her lower lip. 'Lydia, there can be no question....'

'He asks for you all the time, wants to know why we have not brought you to him. Oh, Lauren, don't you see? Andreas is afraid that you were in the car when he crashed, that you are dead, and we are keeping it from him.'

Lauren watched a gull which had flown up from the river, white wings effortless, soaring and drifting on the warm tide of air flowing up from a factory a block away. It had a lazy power which her mind registered absently. She could not conceive of Andreas as anything but strongly vital. Death was an empty concept in her picture of him. He had always been too vibrantly alive.

'I know he has treated you badly,' Lydia went on, and the remark made Lauren's lips twist in bitter amusement.

'What an understatement!' The retort emerged before she had thought about it.

'But he's dying! You can't refuse to see him, Lauren. You know you can't.'

Lauren did know and it made her angry again to face that fact, her eyes savage as she stared out of the window.

'I'll send a car,' Lydia went on quickly. 'All you have to do is stand by his bed for a few moments to let him see you're safe. That won't kill you, will it, Lauren?' There was a faint sarcasm there, Lauren noted, surprised, since Lydia was always so gentle.

'All right,' she said wearily, and Lydia sighed with

relief. Lauren replaced the telephone and stared at the sky. Rain had begun to fall, a thin sleetlike drizzle which blew against the window like tapping fingers. She had not seen Andreas for five years. It had been a long struggle to erase his image from her subconscious. She had dreamt of him night after night for years, despising herself for her inability to control her mind.

They had met when she was still so young, plastic and yielding in her inexperience of life, taking the powerful stamp of his older, stronger personality upon her own nature without even being aware of what was happening to her. Andreas had, in so many senses of the word, possessed her, making her his creature, moulding her as if he were a sculptor with virgin clay, enjoying the sensation of total mastery over her. It had been a bitter civil war within herself when she tried to shake off his domination.

In many ways he had been her opposite—as dark as she had been fair, controlled where she was volatile, fierce and unyielding where she was sensitive and easily hurt. It had been madness in her ever to be drawn to him, but she had fluttered into his presence like a moth pulled by a brilliant light, uncaring if her wings were singed, and Andreas had seized her ruthlessly.

In her innocence she had imagined that his reactions must be the same as her own, that Andreas, too, must feel the heady joy of absolute surrender to love. She had lived on dreams for a long, long time, and the awakening had been indescribably bitter.

Lately she had begun to believe that she had escaped him. They would never meet again and she need not fear him even in her dreams. And now this ... she bit her lip, stifling a groan. She could refuse to go, of course. But, if he were truly dying ... could she?

Dying, she thought with a wild incredulity. Andreas, dying? It wasn't possible. She could not face the prospect of a world in which he did not exist. Even to hate him gave a reason for living.

She had always been fond of Lydia, the only member of the Keralides family to offer her affection or welcome. After the divorce she had regretted having to stop seeing her, but she had seen it as inevitable, although Lydia had protested. Lydia's first loyalty was to Andreas. They could not have met without mentioning his name, and Lauren had had no wish to hear him mentioned, to be reminded of him in any way.

There had been a period when Lydia had rung her constantly in an effort to persuade her to see Andreas, but Lauren had been adamant, and at last Lydia had given up, accepting that it was all over.

Breaking out of the cruel circle of her thoughts she looked down at her paint-stained smock and jeans. She must change. Covering her painting, she went into the bathroom, stripped and showered, then took down a dark green woollen dress from her wardrobe and slid into it, zipping it carefully.

When the knock came she was ready, her blonde hair pleated at the back of her head, leaving her long nape exposed, her oval face cool and controlled, only a slight darkness in the green eyes, their stare fixed, to betray any emotion.

When she opened the door she stared as a young man stepped forward, frowning. 'Hello, Lauren.'

'Is it. . . .' She could not quite believe it, he had been a gangling youth of fifteen when they last met. 'Stephanos?' Where were the ungainly limbs, the pimples, the smooth cheeks? Staring, she saw he was a young man of twenty; slim, elegant, his black hair curling down to his collar, his likeness to his brother far more apparent than it had been before. She had seen photographs of Andreas at this age, and the similarity was striking. 'How are you?' she asked him.

'I am well,' he said with a gritty sound. He had always been very attached to Andreas. His emotion was not surprising. But then they were a very close-knit family, the Keralides, their relationships tightly woven and exclusive. Lauren had found it very hard at first to fit into that family structure. There had been resentment, hostility and even jealousy at first. Gradually she had felt she was wearing it down, but in the end it had defeated her.

He took the suede coat she was carrying and helped her into it. 'It is raining. I have an umbrella, but we will have to run to the car when we get outside.'

He guided her along the corridor to the door of the apartments. When he opened the door rain blew in at them, making her turn her head. Stephanos stepped out, opened his umbrella and she ran with him under it to the long, sleek automobile at the curb. As she reached it he swung open the passenger door and she slid inside, grateful to be out of the rain. Stephanos came round, closed the umbrella and got in beside her.

It was a long time since she had been in a car as luxurious as this one. She looked ironically at the white leather upholstery, the gleaming dashboard whose controls looked as intricate as those on a jumbo jet. Stephanos slicked back his long hair and turned to glance at her.

'You look even more beautiful than I remember, Lauren.' There was a gleam of admiration in his dark eyes as they slid over her, lingering on the long, slenderly curved legs beneath the hem of her dress.

She might have found his masculine interest amusing if it had not reminded her only too forcibly of the first time she met Andreas. 'How is he?' she asked brusquely. 'Have you seen him?'

Stephanos drew back, his features tightening. 'I have seen him,' he nodded. 'What can I say? He looks terrible. I felt sick when I stood at his bed and saw what had happened to him. Andreas was always so strong, so fit. Now he is a broken man.'

She shivered. 'I'm sorry.'

'Are you, Lauren?' Stephanos stared at her almost angrily. 'I wonder.'

Her eyes widened. 'What is that supposed to mean?'

'You hate him. I don't blame you, you have reason, but please, don't pretend a grief you do not feel. With Mama, if you like. She is soft-hearted enough to believe you could still care, but I cannot bear hypocrisy. If I were in Andreas's shoes, even if I was dying, I wouldn't want you pretending to cry at my bedside.'

Her green eyes flashed vividly at him. 'I've never been a good enough actress to pretend anything, Stephanos. I'm coming to see your brother because your mother begged me to—for myself, I agree with you. It's a ridiculous idea for me to see Andreas again. If he was in his right mind I would never consider it.

But Lydia asked me to and I'm very fond of your mother.'

Stephanos had the grace to look ashamed, his face flushed, his eyes embarrassed. 'I'm sorry, I shouldn't have spoken as I did. I had no right.'

'I agree, you had no right whatever.'

Her tone deepened his flush. He put an apologetic hand on her arm. 'Lauren, please. I am truly sorry. It is just the shock of seeing Andreas like that. It has made me feel that nothing is safe, nothing is certain. Andreas has always been the rock of the family, the strongest of us all. He has been a father to me since my own died.'

Lauren stiffened at that, her mouth compressing. She wanted no reminders of Giorgios Keralides. He had been her enemy from the very beginning. The last time she saw him she had been bitterly insulted, humiliated. His death a few months later had not softened her feelings towards him an inch.

'Shouldn't we get on?' she asked tightly.

'Yes, yes, of course.' Stephanos started the car. It surged with power like a sleek panther then sped away with the rain running down the windows, making it hard to see more than a short distance in front of them.

'Unless you want to end in the same hospital as your brother I suggest you slow down,' she said sharply.

'Sorry.' The engine roar dropped away and they drove at a more sedate pace, the click of the windshield wipers sounding softly in the silence between them. Stephanos lit a thin black cigar at the car lighter. Glancing at her, he said uncertainly, 'You don't object?'

'No,' she said shortly.

After a moment she asked him: 'What are you doing now, Stephanos? Working in the firm?'

'Of course.' He smiled hesitantly at her, his features filled with charm. 'What else?'

'What else,' she echoed sardonically.

'I work here in London.' He stared ahead at the road.

'Oh? I didn't know. How long have you been over here?'

'A year. I spent a year in New York with Andreas first, then he sent me here to get some more experience.'

'Do you like living in London?'

Stephanos grimaced. 'It isn't Athens.'

'No,' she smiled drily.

'I miss the sunshine.'

'Will you be going back to New York or staying here?'

He shrugged his broad shoulders. 'That's up to Andreas.' There was a silence stiff with unspoken thoughts, then he said huskily, 'If he lives.'

'Of course he will live!' She spoke angrily, her eyes brilliant. 'Don't take a defeatist attitude, Stephanos. Andreas would never permit it if he knew. You have to believe that he'll get better.'

'You don't believe it or you wouldn't be here.'

The simplicity of the retort shook her. She looked at the road, breathing deeply because tears threatened to flood her eyes. He was right, of course. She had been pretending to be calm, but underneath she was filled with agonised misery which she dared not admit.

The car swung into a curved drive. An ambulance blocked their path for a moment. Stephanos ground out his cigar while he waited, his finger tips drumming on the wheel. 'I'm sorry,' he said gently, not looking at her.

The car moved forward again and stopped outside the glass-doored entrance. He slid out, came round and helped her out, his hand under her elbow. 'I must go and park,' he said. 'Wait here. I won't be a minute.'

The rain had stopped but the sky had a grey, livid light, as though more rain was harboured in the pressing clouds. The pavement had a wet shine to it and the overhang of the entrance dripped slowly in a quiet melancholy.

Stephanos came back and took her arm again. 'This way.' They walked into the crowded foyer and he guided her towards a lift at the back of the room. A few other people crowded in after them as they entered the lift. It rose jerkily and stopped. 'Excuse me,' Stephanos said, clearing a way for them. Lauren followed him blindly, her heart beating so hard she wondered that everyone within earshot could not hear it.

She had not seen him for five years.

The corridor had a cool antiseptic smell, the floor a smooth blue vinyl into which her high heels seemed to sink as though it were quicksand. There were few noises. A row of identical blue doors faced them. She allowed Stephanos to lead her to one of them and stood, shaking, as he opened it.

The room revealed was a waiting-room. She saw that in a flickering look. Her body sagged as she realised it. Then Lydia was running towards her, arms outstretched.

'Lauren! Oh, my dear!'

They clung, cheeks pressed together, Lydia's black head a few inches below Lauren's sleek blonde one. She had forgotten how very small Lydia was, she thought. In her arms the older woman had the tiny bones and delicate build of a child. Pulling away, Lauren looked at her and saw the brown, weathered skin, the very black eyes which held a tender sadness, the straight nose and pale mouth. Lydia looked older. Five years ago she had been a middle-aged woman who contrived at times to look like a young one. Now she was old. Time had fallen upon her like a wolf, devouring her substance. She had lost weight, her cheeks hollowed, her eyes very deepset beneath their thin black brows.

'How I've missed you,' Lydia said huskily, trying to smile.

'I've missed you.' The admission was not easy. Lauren had not wanted to feel so much. Her voice was rough, almost unkind.

Lydia caught the note in it and smiled at her almost compassionately. 'How ironic life can be, that at last you should be here with us but for such a terrible reason!'

Lauren glanced at the other people in the room. Sybil she knew at once, she had not altered an inch, not a hair. She sat there stolidly, the only daughter of the house, her full face calm and giving nothing away, her dark eyes expressionless. She was a few years older than Lauren, married to a Greek lawyer. Their marriage had been a happy one. The last time Lauren heard, they had four children; three sons and a daughter. They would not, however, bear the name Keralides and they did not count. Sybil knew that and resented it. She had resented Lauren because any child she bore would be a Keralides.

Gregori sat beside Sybil. He looked prosperous, well-fed, his broad shoulders fitting perfectly beneath his expensively cut suit. His curly black hair curled over his wide forehead and overshadowed his dark eyes. Andreas had a love-hate relationship with his cousin. Gregori was, however, a Keralides—the son of one of the three brothers, working in the far-flung Keralides empire, moving from New York to Paris, from Paris to Athens. He had not been Lauren's enemy, far from it. Once or twice he had made his admiration only too clear and she had been forced to snub him rather coldly. It had seemed to amuse him. Now he was smiling at her and murmuring a greeting to which she replied quietly.

A small boy sat beside Gregori, hand snuggled in his, and with one look she knew who he was, her heart winced inside her.

Lydia saw her looking at the child. 'Niko,' she said softly, and the boy slid down from his chair, came running to her.

Lydia put a hand on his small round black head, facing him towards Lauren. 'Lauren, this is Niko. Niko, this is Lauren.' The words had a strangely ritualistic ring about them and Lauren was half angry, half moved as she looked down into the face staring up at her.

His father's image, she thought. The Keralides eyes, black, slanting, lashed with thick sooty lashes that curled upwards silkily; hair with the blackbird sheen, straight proud nose, cheekbones high and hauntingly similar, only his soft pink little mouth still too youthful and delicate to remind her of the mouth which had once bruised hers into breathless submission.

'Hallo, Niko,' she said quietly.

His hand came out politely and she took it, painfully surprised by the pleasure it gave her to feel the small fingers inside her own.

His eyes measured her, probed into her own, as though he knew all about her, but surely to God they had told him nothing? He was straight and slender, tall for four, his chin already aggressively male, with a determined thrust which was only too reminiscent of his father. She felt a peculiar craving to pick him up and hold him in her arms, close to her, kiss his skin, that smooth olive complexion which was faintly brushed with pink along the line of his cheekbones.

Sybil came forward, resentment in every line of her, and turned him back towards the seat. Lydia looked after her daughter, mouth wry, giving a sigh. 'Will you come and see him now?' she asked, turning to Lauren.

In the corridor Lydia halted and gave her a troubled look, her lashes flickering. 'You will be careful, won't you?'

Lauren's mouth tightened. 'I'm not going to attack him, if that's what you mean.'

Lydia clicked her tongue. 'Don't be flippant, please. Not now. I realise you're under a strain, but so are we all.'

Lauren grimaced. 'I'm sorry.'

Lydia leant forward and kissed her cheek. 'He's so weak, Lauren. You'll see what I mean. He is too weak to say much, don't let him talk, just smile at him.'

Smile! Lauren groaned inwardly. Did Lydia have any idea what she was asking? She ran a hand through her hair and Lydia's dark eyes stared at the diamond which flashed as she moved her fingers.

'You can't wear that,' she burst out.

For a few seconds Lauren's face was blank as she stared back, not comprehending, then her face flushed deeply as she looked at the diamond ring on her left hand.

'If he saw that,' Lydia groaned.

'I'm engaged to be married,' Lauren said stubbornly.

Lydia looked distraught, her lower lip trembling. 'Lauren, don't you understand? He thinks you're still his wife.'

'He's wrong, then,' said Lauren, and there was burning resentment in her voice.

'You've got to pretend it's true just for a few moments,' Lydia cried with a sort of anguish. 'It would be too much of a shock to tell him the truth, Lauren. He isn't strong enough. Anything could tip the balance. Do you want his death on your conscience?'

'Oh, God!' Lauren groaned, her green eyes fierce. 'You ask a good deal, Lydia.' Slowly she drew the ring off her finger. 'There. I hope you're satisfied.'

Lydia looked at her uneasily, visibly hesitating. With a wry grimace, Lauren asked: 'Well, what now?'

Lydia fumbled in her purse, then slowly extended her hand, palm upwards. Lauren flinched from what lay there. 'No,' she said hoarsely. 'I won't!'

'He's dying,' Lydia said again, accusingly. 'You can't refuse. I won't let you.' Despite her gentle nature there was strength in her now, anger and determination. Lauren shivered and reached for the gold wedding ring. The heavy band slid over her knuckle. It was a family heirloom, Greek, formed of the entwined bodies of snakes, and had often caused comment among her friends. Five years ago she had taken it off and thrown it across the room at his father. Giorgios had bent and picked it up, smiled coldly. 'Now it will be worn as it was meant to be worn, by the woman Andreas should have married when he married you.'

Lydia slid a hand through her arm, squeezed her gently. 'Thank you, my love. Come now, he is waiting for you. I told him a few moments ago that you were on your way and he was so relieved.'

She opened the door of the room in which he lay and took Lauren's hand, leading her across the shadowy space between door and bed. A nurse in a striped blue and white uniform sat at a little desk. She turned her head, standing up, her eyes curious. Lauren glanced at her briefly before turning her head towards the bed.

Her heart was thudding violently. Perspiration sprang up on her palms, at the back of her neck, between her breasts.

His head lay on the pillowless bed, a swathe of bandages enveloping it. The covers were raised on a cradle, indicating some damage to limbs, and one of his arms was in plaster. Bandages could be seen beneath the jacket of his pyjamas.

She knew she was deliberately noticing the exterior details of his appearance because she was afraid to look into the dark eyes which were now open, visible between the bandages, staring at her intently.

Lydia's hand tugged at her arm imploringly. Lauren was rooted to the spot for a moment, breathing heavily.

'Lauren.' His voice breathed the name almost too faintly to be heard.

She went to the bed slowly, trembling.

'I was afraid you were dead and they were hiding it from me,' he whispered in that hoarse, faint voice, pausing for breath every few words.

'I was away,' she said huskily. 'I came back as soon as I heard.'

He studied her face with the familiar, sardonic glint in his eyes. 'You must not be frightened,' he murmured, mouth indenting. 'I refuse to die.' A smile glimmered in those dark depths. 'When they were evasive about you I did wonder if I could bear to live without you, but now I've seen you I fully intend to walk out of here, *eros mou*.'

The whispered final words made her catch her breath. Her hands went ice cold. Looking back over her shoulder she saw Lydia's watchful, imploring face, white and strained, and guessed that her own features bore that look. Her skin felt like death.

When she looked back at him Andreas searched her face, frowning. 'Aren't you going to kiss me, Lauren?' The sensual, husky way he spoke her name always had made her blush and his eyes flickered mockingly as he saw the colour rise in her cheeks.

Bending her head, her heart drumming, she touched her mouth to his very lightly. She would have straightened at once, but his unhurt arm came up to touch her face, his fingertips stroking her cheek. At close quarters she could see the black pupil rayed with tiny flecks of light which faded into the lustrous darkness of his eyes. His hand dropped suddenly and the eyes closed.

Lydia led her out of the room, an arm around her. 'It happens like that, suddenly. He just falls back into sleep. But this time I think he will sleep properly now he knows you are safe. Thank you, Lauren.'

Lauren turned on her. 'Don't thank me, for God's sake!'

'I realise it was an ordeal for you.'

'An ordeal?' Lauren was trembling, her face a livid white. 'It was hell. What do you think I'm made of? Iron? I had to stand there and kiss him and hear him call me ...' She swallowed. '*Eros mou*,' she spat out furiously. 'God, I wanted to be sick. And you thank me!' She pulled off the heavy gold ring and thrust it at Lydia. 'Take this back. I never want to set eyes on it again. Or on any of you!'

Pushing her way past Lydia, she ran out of the hospital as if the furies were after her, sobbing hoarsely under her breath. In the car park she halted, not knowing which way to go. A taxi, she thought at last. She had to get a taxi. She turned to make her way back to the reception desk to ask if she could telephone for one, but found herself facing Stephanos.

He looked at her in angry pity. 'You look terrible.'

'Leave me alone, Stephanos, please!'

'I'll take you back home.'

'No! I'll take a taxi.'

'Don't be silly. I'll take you.'

She pulled her arm from him. 'Don't you understand? I've had enough. I want to go, to go alone. I've had enough of the Keralides for one day.' She laughed wildly. 'What am I saying? For one day? For a life-time!'

'I do understand,' he said quietly, looking far more mature than his years, his eyes grave. 'But I cannot permit you to drive back to your apartment alone. You are in a distressed condition. You must not be left alone, Lauren. Lydia ordered me to stay with you until you are back to your home.'

She would have pulled away from him again, but he would not allow her to struggle her way free. He led her at last to his car and put her into it. The drive back was even more silent than the one on their way to the hospital. Outside her apartment building, he looked at her as he switched off the ignition.

'Lauren, my mother wanted me to say ...'

'I don't want to hear,' she cried desperately, pulling open the door. She was out of the car before he had time to realise it. He got out and came round towards her, but by then she was inside the building. She found her key and let herself into her apartment, shut the door and leaned against it, breathing deeply.

Tears began to run down her white face. Stephanos knocked and called in vain. Lauren could not have moved if she tried. At last she heard his footsteps as he walked away. Then she slowly slid to the floor in a faint.

CHAPTER TWO

PHILIP stood in her studio staring at the canvas with his brown head on one side, the soberly intent look of his eyes caressing. 'You get better every day. You're going to outshine Jimmy one of these days. Do you realise that?'

'Does Jimmy?' She laughed, green eyes dancing.

'Of course he knows, he knew before any of us, he always said you were going to be good.' Philip moved closer and peered at the thin line of stark trees sketched in along one side of the painting. 'I like that. Incredible the way they look so solid from a distance and get more and more vague the closer you get.'

'You're not supposed to stand with your nose pressed against them.'

He turned and grinned at her. 'Darling, I like to see.'

'So you do,' she smiled back, and went into his arms easily to lift her face for his kiss. He put both arms round her, holding her, touching his lips to her nose, her cheeks, her eyes.

'You're impossible, Lauren.'

'What do you mean?' She opened her eyes wide.

'So beautiful and so clever. It isn't fair.'

She laughed. 'To whom?'

'Every other female on this earth.' Philip's eyes twinkled, the lines of humour around them stretching and dissolving.

She looked at him affectionately, leaning against him in a trusting way, her arms round his waist. 'I do love you,' she whispered.

His brow rose. 'When I pay you compliments?'

'Every second of the day,' she insisted, wrinkling her nose.

'That's what I like to hear.' He lifted an arm and glanced at his wristwatch over her shoulder. 'I must go. I've got a client at eleven.'

She sighed. 'Must you? It's so comforting to have you here. I've barely seen you this week.' She had needed to see him, especially after visiting Andreas. The memory made her look at him through her lashes. She hadn't told him yet. She had meant to, but she found it hard to explain, although, God knew, it was a simple enough story, but any mention of Andreas Keralides always made Philip angry.

'When we're married things will be different,' he promised gently. His eyes were amused. 'Very different.'

Lauren had known him all her life and she felt no urgency to become his wife but she did feel a warmth whenever she was with him. She felt it now as he drew away from her.

He was not a handsome man. He lacked the dark vibrancy which made Andreas a compelling figure. Lauren, however, found his rugged face and calm smile essentially attractive. She enjoyed his company, was always happy to see him. Philip had been in love with her for years, even during her marriage. She had always known it. He had made no secret of his feelings. But only in the recent year had she turned to him at last, finding in him the security she needed.

'Jimmy is flying back from Spain in two days,' he said on his way to the door.

'I know, he sent me a telegram. It was rather chaotic, but it did say he was coming back.' She laughed. 'It must have cost him a fortune! It was more a letter than a telegram, all jumbled phrases.'

Philip grinned. 'His work is going well.'

'That explains it. Did he cable you, too?'

'I got a phone call. Half of it was Spanish and I didn't understand a word of that, but I gathered he was flying back. Who is Emma, though?'

Lauren frowned. 'Emma? I've no idea. Did he mention an Emma?'

'Several times, but I never got the connection.'

She shrugged. 'You know my dear father. She's probably a model.'

Philip grinned. 'Sorry I asked.'

She pinched him. 'Why? I'm a big girl now. The days when Jimmy hid his model girl-friends from me have long gone. I wonder if she can cook. Good lord, remember Pascale? She cooked like a dream.'

'A good model, too,' said Philip, reminiscence in his face. 'Those fantastic shoulders of hers.'

His eyes met Lauren's and they both burst out laughing. 'You fraud,' she teased. 'Shoulders indeed!'

He opened the door. 'I keep forgetting you're un-shockable,' he returned as teasingly.

'After living with Jimmy all my life? How could I be shocked?'

Philip paused, a slight frown on his face. 'There's not a jealous bone in your body, is there, Lauren? It's admirable.' Yet he sounded piqued, his eyes disturbed.

His words made her start, her eyes darkening. He bent and kissed her, then was gone, and she walked back into her studio, standing by the window in the bright autumnal sunshine, staring out at the blue sky. The weather had changed in the last few days. The rain and wind which had prevailed for two days had gone. Only the bare trees, their last leaves wrenched from them during the storm, belied the summery brilliance of the sky. Saturated, torn, they lay in heaps of brown and grey, across the pavements and in the gutters of the London street.

Not a jealous bone in her body! How little Philip knew! She thought of the savage grinding emotions which had once tortured her and her hands went to her stomach as though they ate her again, her clenched fists thrust against her body.

Her eyes shut. 'God!' Her voice sounded strange, alien, in the sunny room.

She had heard nothing more from any member of the Keralides family since she ran out of the hospital the day she saw Andreas. Presumably he had regained his memory. She had seen nothing in the newspapers about his death, just a paragraph saying that he had had a car crash and been injured. The story had been calm, playing down his injuries, which had not surprised her, since she knew the lengths to which his family would go to ensure privacy for their members, particularly since any rumour of Andreas's death could cause a stampede on the stock market and send a tremor of alarm around the whole world.

She had thought of ringing the hospital to find out

how he was, but although her hand had hovered over the receiver for minutes on end she had at last resisted the temptation. If he did die she was certain she would be informed of it.

It had not been easy to fight the temptation. Seeing him again had opened up old wounds, making them bleed afresh. Lauren had not slept well since. Even her dreams had been filled with him. Only her pride kept her from going back there just to see him once more, even if only for a moment, and the husky sound of his voice whispering, '*Eros mou....*' went on and on inside her head. She had never imagined she would ever hear him speak those words again.

She turned away angrily and picked up her sketch-book. Eyes dark, she began to work quickly. The face grew beneath her fingers and she stopped after a while to stare at it, seeing for the first time what she was doing. Niko's delicate childish features stared up at her and she winced.

Her subconscious was treacherous, she thought. She moved to tear the page from the pad and rip it to pieces, but just then there was a knock at the door. She put down the pad and went to open it.

Lydia confronted her gently, ruthlessly, her thin face determined. Lauren sighed.

'What do you want, Lydia?'

The dark eyes were steady. 'Don't you want to know if he is alive or dead?'

Lauren's mouth compressed. 'If he were dead I would have heard. The world would know.'

Lydia shook her head reproachfully. 'How can you

be so cruel? He needs you. Come to him. Why have you stayed away?'

Lauren ran both hands through her smooth hair, destroying the sleek style, sending pale tendrils tumbling around her face. 'Lydia, have some pity, for God's sake!'

'I wish I did not have to ask it of you, but Andreas comes first with me, Lauren.'

'He always did. Andreas comes first with everybody.'

'So bitter.' Lydia gazed at her, dark eyes wide. 'He has been unconscious most of the time since you visited him so I did not think it was necessary to call you, but now he is awake, wide awake, and he is asking for you again.'

Lauren whitened. 'You mean he still hasn't remembered?'

Lydia shook her head.

'My God!' Lauren turned back into the room and Lydia followed her, staring about her curiously, observing the neat condition of the paints and utensils, the range of stacked canvases against the wall.

'So this is where you work! You have begun to be successful. That much I have heard myself. Your father must be proud of you.'

'Yes, he is.' Lauren walked to the window and stared out. 'I can't come, Lydia. If he's stronger, now is the time to tell him.'

'And kill him?' The voice was soft but remorseless.

'It wouldn't do that!'

'You heard what he said the other day. Without you he would not want to live.'

Lauren turned on her heel, trembling, eyes accusing.

'We both know he's lived without me for five years. He won't die now because he merely remembers that I'm no longer his wife.'

'He does not remember, though. And the shock of being told might do some irreparable damage.'

'Andreas is stronger than that.' Her mouth tormented, Lauren laughed. 'He's as tough as leather.'

'He was once. Now he is very weak, very frail, hanging on to life by a thread, and I refuse to cut that thread by telling him something he does not want to hear.'

Their eyes met and Lauren drew a shaky breath. 'Doesn't want to hear? What do you mean?'

'Ah, Lauren,' Lydia murmured. 'You know precisely what I mean. I have had a psychiatrist's opinion on the matter. Andreas has not merely lost his memory. He is refusing to remember.'

Moving restlessly, Lauren said: 'Why should he? I know what you're trying to do, Lydia, but it won't work. You have to accept that Andreas and I are finished, have been for five years. His accident can't alter that. In three months I'm getting married again. You know that.'

Ignoring her last remarks, Lydia said huskily, 'Andreas is defending himself, that is what the specialist said. He knows how ill he is, he realises he may die, and he is going back in time to the days when he was happy with you. It makes him feel safer. It gives him a reason for living.'

Lauren stood very still, staring at her. 'Do you know what you're saying? It isn't true.'

'My dear, I am certain of it. Andreas has not lost his memory entirely, only his memory of the years since he lost you. He has blocked it all out. Even Niko, his son, whom he loves dearly, believe me. Andreas would not lightly refuse to recognise his own son. He adores the boy. Yet he looked at him without a flicker and said: "Who is it?"'

Lauren frowned, biting her lip. 'Poor child! Was he very hurt?'

Lydia sighed. 'He was upset, yes, but I got him out of there before Andreas could see it. I explained to Niko that the injury to his father's head had made him lose his memory, and I think he accepts that.'

Turning away, Lauren wrapped her arms around herself as though she were suddenly freezing cold. 'All the same, I can't come there again.'

Lydia moved to where the sketch pad lay open. She picked it up and looked at the drawing incredulously. 'This is good, so good. How clever you are, Lauren!'

Lauren turned and flushed, seeing it in the other woman's hands. 'Oh, it was just a sketch from memory.'

'You have caught his face exactly.' Lydia looked at her. 'May I have it? I would treasure it, Lauren. Please!'

Lauren made a gesture, her cheeks hot. 'Of course.'

'Thank you.' Lydia looked at her again, pleading, eyes wet. 'Please come to him, Lauren.'

Lauren saw that she had no alternative. Lydia had an immovable look. She would stay there until Lauren gave in. 'Oh, very well.'

In the car Lydia asked her: 'What did your fiancé say when you told him about Andreas?'

'I didn't tell him.' The reply was brusque and Lauren did not look at her.

Lydia gave her a quick look. 'He does not know about the amnesia?'

'I doubt if he even knows about the accident. He hasn't mentioned it to me and I certainly haven't mentioned it to him.'

'You think he would mind?'

Lauren laughed coldly. 'You know very well he would mind. I am engaged to marry him, yet I'm going to stand by the bed of another man and pretend to be his wife. What do you expect Philip to think?'

'From my memory of him, faint though it is, I have always thought him to be a kind and imaginative man. Surely he would understand?'

Lauren glanced at her wryly. 'Oh, Philip is kind, very. And he is imaginative. That is just the point, surely.' Did Lydia not know that Philip had detested Andreas from first setting eyes on him?

She remembered that evening six years ago as if it were yesterday. Jimmy's biggest exhibition to date, it had been well publicised and very well attended. Some of the canvases had been sold already on that first evening. The smart, jewelled women parading round the room had fluttered as Andreas Keralides appeared in the doorway. Behind him stood two men in dark suits, their faces wooden. Lauren had been standing with Philip at the far end of the long gallery. From a distance she had watched the black-haired figure move from canvas to canvas.

'Who *is* that?' she had asked, smiling with amusement as she watched women eye him eagerly.

'You don't know?' Philip grinned at her. 'Andreas Keralides.'

She had gasped. 'Him? He doesn't look like a business tycoon, does he?'

'What does he look like?' Philip was still being amused by her then, his eyes gentle as he watched her face. She had just left school, a tall leggy eighteen-year-old in her first year at art college. Her blonde hair was then worn in a long pigtail down her back. It kept it out of the way and looked neat.

'I'm not sure.' She gazed at the tall, broadshouldered figure in the evening jacket, seeing the hard fierce bone structure with curious and searching eyes. His features were powerfully handsome, the nose straight and fleshless, the eyes deep under their black brows, thick black lashes flickering against his cheekbones. Then he turned and looked at her and her eyes saw the hard mouth with its hint of passionate sensuality which was at such odds with the austere temples.

She flushed, looking away, and Philip moved suddenly, placing his arm around her almost in a gesture of protection, of possession.

He guided her away to another part of the gallery and she went, bemused, still tingling from the impact of those beautiful eyes.

Her father came up to them and clapped Philip on the shoulder, pretending an aggression he did not feel. 'Hallo, bloodsucker.'

Philip grinned at him, affection in his eyes. They had a close, teasing relationship. Philip had run the gallery for five years then. His father had been Jimmy's friend and guide for years before that. Jimmy both admired and respected him and he had transferred all that affection to Philip when the old man died.

While they talked Lauren had wandered away to listen to some of the comments, eavesdropping shamelessly. A tall, thin woman in peach silk clicked her tongue over one of the pictures. 'But what does it mean? It doesn't say a thing to me.'

'Perhaps you aren't listening,' her companion said with a meaningful smile. 'You have to be open to the influences.'

Lauren's mouth quivered in amusement. She turned away and found herself in the path of Andreas Keralides. His dark eyes smiled at her, his brows lifting in silent comment.

'Good evening, Miss Grey,' he murmured in a voice which she knew immediately she would never forget or mistake for that of any other man, the accents deep and slightly foreign.

Her green eyes had opened to their fullest extent, unknowingly, the darkened lashes quivering. 'How do you know my name?' She felt gauche as soon as she had said it, wondering if he thought her nothing but the schoolgirl which her long pigtail made her look.

His face had expressed amusement, one dark brow lifting, his mouth curved in mockery. 'I asked.'

Colour had poured into her face. The thought that he had noticed her sufficiently to be curious about her had had a strange effect on her pulse rate, making her heartbeat drum in her ears.

He watched her as if he enjoyed the sight of her confusion, his dark eyes glinting, and his amusement annoyed her. Defiance had given her eyes sudden brilliance as she stared at him. 'Have you come to buy one of my father's pictures, Mr Keralides?'

'How do you know my name?' he had returned at once, mocking her openly, and she found herself laughing.

'I asked,' she retorted, and his eyes had narrowed abruptly on her, moving from her laughing mouth to her hair, which under the artificial light had a gleam like silver.

She had found herself looking back into the intent dark eyes, her breathing irregular. Slowly he had put out a hand and to her incredulity had released her hair from its plait, flicking it around her flushed face.

'You will always wear your lovely hair loose for me,' he had said very softly.

Her father had brought her up to be independent, self-reliant, used to freedom. She prickled immediately at Andreas Keralides's autocratic belief that his will was paramount. Lifting her round chin she had retorted, 'Oh, will I?'

That sardonic gleam had come into the dark eyes. 'Oh, yes,' he had whispered, moving closer, watching her with the amused satisfaction of a collector who has seen a rare specimen for his trophy room.

'Why should I?' she had asked, bristling.

His eyes teased her. 'So that when I make love to you I can run my fingers through it, of course.'

Her breath had caught audibly. 'Oh!' she had gasped.

'Oh, indeed,' he had agreed.

'What makes you think I shall let you make love to me?' She had recovered quickly, but her voice had a slight tremor, and he noticed, she knew that by the mockery in his eyes.

'Why not? We'll both enjoy it.'

'I'm not in the habit of letting strangers make love to me, Mr Keralides,' she had told him, and he had laughed.

'I should hope not, but this is different.'

'Why?' she had asked crossly. 'Because you're a millionaire, I suppose?'

He had paused very briefly, moving closer, then he had said, so softly that she thought at first she was mistaken, 'Because I am going to marry you.'

Lauren could still recall her dazed disbelief, her wide-eyed amazement as she stared back at his dark, sardonic face. She had not believed him, then, of course. Belief had come later.

The car had drawn up outside the hospital. Lauren followed Lydia into the foyer and then into the lift. Outside Andreas's room Lydia stopped. 'The ring,' she said apologetically.

Lauren's hand shook as she exchanged rings. Lydia opened the door and whispered, 'I will wait for you in the waiting-room.'

Lauren turned in disturbed surprise, but already the thin straight little figure was moving away down the corridor. After a moment Lauren walked into the room. There was no nurse at the bedside today. The room was silent and empty, the lowered blinds leaving a cool shadow of bars across the white vinyl floor.

The bandaged figure on the bed did not move as she approached. She quietly stood beside him staring down at him. The thick black lashes lay against the white muslin, his lids having a bruised look. Her eyes dropped to the straight pale mouth, then she bent as though unable to resist the temptation and touched her own mouth to his.

At once his hand came up from the bed and curved round her neck. She looked up and saw the lids drawn back from the dark eyes.

'Lauren,' he whispered. '*Eros mou*—at last. Where have you been?'

'You look much better,' she said a little unsteadily, trying to move away without hurting him, but his hand had a surprising strength and he would not let her go.

'Kiss me again,' he said huskily. 'I was asleep. That was unfair. I want always to be awake when you kiss me.'

She kissed him lightly, but his hand pressed against her nape, holding her there while his mouth moved hungrily against hers.

She had never imagined she would ever again feel this surge of passionate need. It hurt so fiercely that she had to get away, breaking from his clasp, standing there with her hands clasped together, breathing as if she had been running.

'What is it?' He shifted restlessly and she saw the flicker of pain in his eyes.

'You must lie still,' she said. 'It's bad for you to be upset.'

'I will be very upset if you are cold with me,' he said, teasing her now, just a little, his eyes bright with sensual feeling as they ran over her. 'You look older in this light. Must those blinds stay down? I can barely see you. Come closer.

Lauren turned and pulled up the chair which stood near the bed, sat down on it, keeping her head well back. He would notice a change in her. He would be basing his memory on a girl of nineteen and she was now a woman of twenty-four.

'I mustn't stay long,' she said nervously.

'You have only just come.' He sounded terse, his eyes angry. 'What is it, Lauren? Why are you so distant?'

She summoned all her courage, leaning forward to smile at him. 'I'm sorry if I sound distant. I've been so worried.'

His face relaxed. 'Of course. Poor darling! I am sorry if I have made you unhappy. You're so young to bear a burden like this, *eros mou*. It must all be hard for you.' He lifted his free hand to his head, his eyes filled with impatience. 'How did it happen? I can't remember a thing. They won't tell me, either, except that I crashed the car.'

He sounded ill, he sounded weak, but he did not sound as though he were dying, she thought. He was perfectly rational, perfectly clear.

'A lorry had spilt oil and you skidded on it.'

He frowned. 'When was this? The last thing I can remember is our trip to New York. I recall driving back from Heathrow. You were in the car. That wasn't when we crashed, was it?'

Her throat hurt. She swallowed. 'I wasn't with you when you crashed.'

He stared at her, his eyes searching his face. 'No, Mama said you weren't, I remember. Why did you take so long getting here? Where were you?' His eyes narrowed. 'With Jimmy, I suppose? And your dear friend Philip?'

She stood up, the chair scraping back over the vinyl floor. 'You should try to sleep now, Andreas. I promised only to stay for five minutes.'

'Lauren!' His hand came out and caught at her skirt, clung to it. 'Stay here. You haven't answered me. Were you with Philip Colby?'

There was shock and pain in her eyes. 'No,' she said, because she did not know what else to do. 'Of course not. I was staying with Marie-Claire in Paris.'

He relaxed. 'Oh.' He sighed. 'I'm sorry, darling.'

'Now I really must go.'

'Kiss me,' he whispered.

She had to, but it was agony. His hand caressed the nape, beneath her silky hair, his fingertips stroking it tenderly, he made her kiss him deeply, his mouth opening to explore hers with a hunger which made her shake. He lay back, sighing.

He looked so exhausted that tenderness moved inside her. 'Promise me you'll sleep now,' she begged.

He half-smiled. 'Promise,' he murmured in a faint voice, and before she had left his side he was already sliding into a deep sleep.

Lydia had a short, bouncy little man with her whose well-cut suit and assertive manner proclaimed him to be someone of importance. The self-satisfied look in his eyes underlined that. He smiled and held out his hand. 'Ah, Mrs Keralides, very happy to meet you, very happy indeed.'

'I'm Miss Grey,' Lauren said sharply, looking at Lydia.

'This is Mr Cardew, the specialist who has been called in to take over Andreas's case,' Lydia explained.

Lauren looked at him. 'You're a psychiatrist?'

'Among other things,' he said cheerfully. He peered at her curiously. 'How did you find your husband?'

'We're divorced,' Lauren said firmly.

He smiled. 'He doesn't think so.'

'Whatever he thinks, we are.'

'Legally you may be, but if he will not accept it, then you're still bound.'

'That's absurd!'

He gave her a very shrewd smile. 'But you are here, Mrs Keralides, which indicates that you accept that he still feels bound to you.'

Her colour ebbed away and she looked stricken. 'I came because his mother begged me to.'

'Nevertheless, whatever reason you give yourself, you came. Which says to me that you are bound to him, too.'

'No,' said Lauren, her hands clenched at her sides.

The little man turned a smile towards Lydia. 'I think it would be a good idea for me to talk to Mrs Keralides alone.' He took Lauren's arm. 'Would you come along to my office?'

'I'll wait for you, dear,' said Lydia.

Lauren wearily followed the specialist through a maze of white-walled corridors to his airy green-painted office. He offered her a chair and sat down on the other side of his desk, smiling at her, his eyes probing.

'Your husband has no memory of his accident, you know.'

She nodded. 'He told me.'

'Did he tell you what his last memory was?'

Her eyes were brilliant with pain. 'Yes.'

'Will you tell me?'

She shrugged. 'I really don't see. . . .'

'Please!'

Sighing, she said, 'He remembers us coming back from a trip we made to New York.'

'When was that?'

'Just over five years ago.'

'Was there any significance in that for you?'

Her smile froze on her mouth. Significance, she thought. Oh, yes, there was significance. After a moment she said huskily, 'The day after we got back my husband and I had a terrible quarrel. I left him and went back to my father and he. . . .' She could not go on. Her voice broke and her lips trembled as tears sprang into her eyes.

The little man leaned forward, hands on the desk, staring at her thoughtfully. 'And he?' he prompted.

'He was unfaithful to me,' she said at last, biting the words out with her teeth almost together.

There was a silence. 'Did you discover this?'

She nodded. She had stayed with Jimmy just that one night and in the morning she had known how stupidly she had behaved. She had taken a taxi back to her house in the early morning, filled with contrition and love, run up the stairs to Andreas's bedroom, their bedroom, opened the door and stood there as if someone had shot her through the heart.

From the pillow beside Andreas's dark head Martine had lifted her flushed face, smiling. She hadn't said a word. The smile had become laughter, the dark eyes had mocked and derided.

Lauren had turned without a sound and walked back

out of the house. Andreas had come to see her later that day, but Jimmy had refused to admit him. From her room she had heard the raised voices, the anger. Andreas tried to force his way into the house, then Philip arrived. The fight had been brutal. She had heard every second of it, shuddering and feeling sick. Together Philip and Jimmy had evicted Andreas, though. The next day Lauren had been on a flight to Scotland to stay with her aunt in Inverness. From there she had instructed her solicitor. Andreas had written to her and she had returned his letters, unopened. The divorce was filed in America, since that was where they had married, and a bare week after it was finalised Andreas married Martine. Her son was born three weeks later. Niko, the boy on whose flesh Andreas had stamped his own image so unmistakably. There could never be any question as to his paternity.

'And you divorced him?' The specialist's question made her jump. She turned dazed eyes on him.

'Yes,' she said wearily.

'Have you seen him since the day you left him?'

She shook her head.

He scratched his chin, a faint smile on his mouth. 'An open and shut case, isn't it?'

'Is it?'

'Come now, Mrs Keralides. . . .'

'Don't call me that!'

He eyed her thoughtfully. 'My dear young lady, what's in a name? There can be no question about it, can there? Your husband bitterly regrets that divorce, the whole subject of what followed the day you left him. He has expunged it from his memory because in his present state he's subconsciously aware that he can't face it. Until his bodily strength returns, I suspect his memory will not return.'

Lauren wished she could dispute what he said, but common sense made it too reasonable. 'What then?' she asked him. 'We can't go on pretending like this. I'm engaged to another man.'

He nodded. 'So I understand. How long have you been engaged?'

'Just over a week.'

The shrewd eyes widened. 'Indeed? How interesting!'

Lauren stared at him. Why was he smiling like that?

'Was your engagement announced in the press?'

'Of course.' Jimmy's fame and Philip's ownership of the gallery had made it a newsworthy item. Several papers had carried little stories about it.

'Do you recall the day on which the stories appeared?'

She frowned irritably. 'The day we got engaged, I suppose ... oh, no, the next day.' Her voice broke off and she stared at him. Slowly she said, 'The day Andreas crashed.'

He smiled, well satisfied. 'Precisely. I suspected as much. As I said, an open and shut case. Almost too neat.'

'Far too neat,' she said huskily. 'I don't believe it.'

'And have you some other explanation?' He put his fingers together as if he were praying, smiling down at them, the smug face undisguised in its satisfied amusement.

She stood up. 'Not at this moment, but I'll work on it.'

He laughed openly. 'Do that, Mrs Keralides.'

She halted and glared at him. 'Has it occurred to you that if the news of my engagement in some way caused Andreas to crash his car then his amnesia has to be deliberate?'

He gave her a large smile. 'Of course, but not necessarily in the way you mean. He isn't pretending, Mrs Keralides. He has genuinely lost all memory of those five years. The mind is almost miraculous in its capacity to shut out painful memories for its own protection. As I say, when he is physically restored, he'll permit his memory to return too.'

'And until then?'

He shrugged. 'I must insist that you don't disillusion him until I allow it. The shock could be very harmful.'

She stared at the floor, biting her lip. 'He isn't going to die. I'm sure of it now. He was far too strong when I saw him today.'

'Shock can kill a perfectly healthy human being, believe me. When a man is as badly injured as your husband was, it's doubly dangerous.'

Lauren closed her eyes. 'Oh, God,' she whispered. 'I don't know how much more of this I can take.'

CHAPTER THREE

AUTUMN was fading into winter slowly with a languorous softness which betrayed itself in early morning mists, mild weather and occasional showers of rain. The temperature remained above normal. Girls still walked about in summer frocks and men wore shirtsleeves in the afternoons. London was enjoying the last taste of summer before grey cold invaded the streets.

Against her better judgment, Lauren continued to visit Andreas at the hospital. Daily she spent half an hour with him, reading newspapers to him, seated by his bed, holding his hand, watching the mocking light come and go in his dark eyes when he looked at her. He teased her gently, as he had in those first months of their marriage, showing her a warm tenderness she remembered with grief.

It was strange, she thought, walking out of the hospital one afternoon, because his moods in the weeks before they went to New York had been dark and brooding and one would have imagined that he would have gone back to the feelings he had had then, but he seemed to be the man she had first married, her passionate, gentle lover.

Those first months of marriage had been heavenly. Andreas had been an exciting lover, sensitive, aware of her innocence and protective of it, while sweeping her away on the tide of his own desire. The only barrier to a perfect happiness had been his father's cold hostility. Giorgios had made no secret of the fact that he had wanted Andreas to marry his cousin Martine, a thin dark Greek girl with sultry, sullen eyes.

Martine contained her jealous anger within a shell of antagonistic silence whenever she was alone with Lauren. In Andreas's presence the girl had been demurely sweet, all smiles and fluttering lashes, and Andreas had treated her with a smiling indulgence which had always raised the hair on Lauren's head. She had suppressed her jealousy, reasoning that if Andreas had loved Martine he would have married her, but jealousy is an instinctive reaction which reason cannot touch. Lauren feared and disliked Martine and it showed.

When the pressures and strains of living in the Keralides household became too great, Lauren retreated to her father's house for a few hours. She had given up art college, to please Andreas, but she felt an itching in her fingers now and then, a need to paint which was inherited and irrepressible.

Jimmy encouraged her, making a corner of his own studio clear so that she could work there, and Philip, overlooking her work, sighed and said it was a crime that someone so talented should be straitjacketed by marriage.

Philip's friendship had not pleased Andreas. His Greek background made it impossible for him to believe that a man could enjoy a woman's friendship without wanting more, and although Lauren laughed at the notion that Philip was in love with her, Andreas finally proved to her that his suspicions were correct.

He came to her father's house to pick her up after one of her long painting sessions. Philip stood aside while Andreas put her into her coat, watching as she lifted her flushed face and her husband kissed her briefly but passionately.

They both turned before Philip had time to control his expression and as they drove away afterwards Andreas said grimly, 'You saw it. Don't lie to me again, Lauren. The man is crazy about you.'

She had not answered because she could not think of anything to say. It had been a shock to her to realise Philip's feelings. For years she had thought of him as an older brother or a young uncle, and it was hard to rearrange those patterns of thinking.

'You must never be alone with him again,' Andreas had said sharply. 'Never!'

Anxiously, she had protested, 'How can I avoid him? He's always welcome at my father's house. They're old friends.'

'Then you must stay away from your father's house.' Andreas had looked hard at her. 'I am sorry if you find this difficult, but your father is welcome to visit you at our home.'

'Our home!' Her eyes had flashed angrily. 'How can it be?'

Andreas's brows had creased, darkness in his eyes. 'What do you mean?'

'We live in your father's home, under his roof, with your brothers and sister always underfoot, and I'm not welcome there—I never have been. They make it plain that I'm an intruder. Why do you think I go so often to see my father? I have to get out of that atmosphere, get away from all that enmity and malice.'

It had been the start of another long row which had ended, as they all did, with Andreas stalking off, dark-browed, leaving her to scuttle after him like a child.

The days of wine and roses had been short, Lauren sighed, arriving back at her apartment. The first heady bliss of life with Andreas had been destroyed bit by bit by the attitude of his family, the difference in their ages, her own inexperience and inability to cope, and her jealousy of Martine.

The trip to New York had been a last desperate attempt to regain their happiness. Andreas had suggested it after one of their rows and she had leapt at it, but although while they were away they had been happy together, the moment they got back to London trouble had begun again. Martine's birthday party was in progress the night they got back. Lauren was tired by the journey and begged off the party, retiring early to bed. Andreas had stayed. Lauren had slept for two hours and woken up after midnight to hear music downstairs. From the landing she had peered down the broad staircase. The huge hall mirror reflected the long saloon to her and gave her an image of Martine, eyes sensuous, drifting around to the music in Andreas's arms. Lauren had gone to bed tense, filled with jealousy, and lain awake for hours. It was four o'clock when she fell asleep and Andreas still had not come to bed, although the house was silent and all the guests departed.

It had, of course, precipitated another quarrel. Giorgios Keralides had walked into the middle of it and sneered at her, 'If you are jealous of Martine, ask yourself why! Is it not because you know she is the woman Andreas should have married, not yourself; a woman of his own kind, not a pretty, ignorant little nobody.'

She had taken off her wedding ring and thrown it at him while Andreas stood there in bitter silence.

She had fled to her father's house, believing that Andreas saw as his father did now, that he regretted their marriage. During the long night she had been visited by contradictory impulses, swinging between love and hatred, jealousy and need, until in the first light she had returned to the Keralides house to make an attempt to win her husband back again, whatever the costs, however she had to abase herself.

The image of what she had found had haunted her night and day for months; Andreas's black head, his face flushed in sleep, his lids closed as he lay entwined with Martine and the girl's smiling, taunting triumph as she looked across the room at Lauren.

Even now it bit into her and she gave a choked gasp of pain. She could never forget it. It had been a knife sliding into her stomach and she felt it even now, a pain which tore and wrenched at her flesh.

She had known, of course, that there had been women before her, but she had innocently believed that that was all over. Andreas had sworn total fidelity and she had kissed his hand in a sort of adoring gratitude. Her own blindness now infuriated her.

She still had not told Philip. Instinct warned her that he would react angrily, perhaps demand that her visits to Andreas cease, and she knew she could not yet bring herself to stop seeing Andreas.

Her work had suffered lately. She seemed to have lost the impulse to paint. She had to force herself to pick up her brush and her hand when she worked had lost its cunning, seemed wooden, unresponsive, reluctant.

Philip arrived that afternoon while she was sighing over the canvas. He stood at her elbow and frowned. 'Something wrong?'

She glanced at him nervously. 'Why do you ask that?'

'My dear girl!' He grimaced, his finger gesturing towards the picture. 'Here ... I've never known you so clumsy. I can see you've reworked that a number of times and it still isn't right, is it?'

There was no point in hiding anything from him. Philip knew more about art than many painters, his eye was impeccable.

'I think it's time I told you something,' she said hesitatingly, and he stiffened, looking hard at her.

'Sit down, Philip.'

'Am I going to need a drink?' he asked drily, and she laughed.

'Want one?'

'Perhaps I should.'

She got him a whisky and he held it in his hand, shifting it, his eyes on the amber liquid. 'Well?'

Lauren told it quickly, huskily, starkly, and saw his face darken and harden.

'Hell, you must be out of your mind!' His eyes held little red flames as though his jealousy were red-hot and she had never seen Philip lose his cool before. It amazed and frightened her.

'You've been visiting him every day for weeks and you've never told me? Lying to me, cheating me.' He sounded breathless as though he could barely enunciate. 'I wouldn't have believed it of you, Lauren.'

'I didn't imagine it would go on so long,' she said miserably. 'The first time they said he was dying and how could I refuse to go then? And then the specialist said he would be in danger if he had a big shock and finding out that we were no longer married could be a shock to him—so what else could I do but play along?'

'You could have told me,' Philip said tersely. 'I would have dealt with it.' His eyes flared, meeting hers. 'That is, if you'd wanted it dealt with, but you didn't, did you, Lauren? You wanted to go on seeing that Greek bastard. You never have got over him, have you? I thought for a while that he was completely forgotten, but the minute he so much as whistles you crawl back to him like a fool and let him use you the way he did before.'

'He's been very ill!'

Philip laughed harshly. 'Very convenient!'

'Philip, he has! He almost died! You didn't see him that first day. He was white and exhausted, he could barely move or speak.'

Philip's lips twitched into an angry sneer. 'He managed to make his needs clear enough, though, didn't he? He got you there.'

'Philip, in common decency, I had to go!'

He took her shoulders in both hands and shook her, her face startled as she stared up at him, her green eyes wide. 'You wanted to go! Admit it!'

Her temper rose as his had done, spiralling up in a

sudden fierce rage. She lost control of her mind and her tongue and shouted back at him. 'All right, I did, I wanted to see him again. I love him!' She cut off the words in an appalled silence and closed her eyes briefly, then looked at Philip sadly. 'I'm sorry, Philip. I can't help it. I don't even want to, but I do, passionately—I'm crazy about him.'

'Yes,' Philip said clearly, coldly. 'Yes, I know. I suppose I've always known. It was obvious from the day he walked into Jimmy's exhibition. One look and you fell all the way. I was a fool to hope it was over.'

She bent her head submissively, filled with bitter regret, then drew her ring off her hand and held it out to him. 'I'm so sorry it had to end like this.'

Philip drew a sharp breath, staring at the ring as if he had never seen it before, then he sighed deeply. 'Look, my dear, I'm sorry I lost my temper. Will you listen to me calmly for a moment?'

She looked up hesitantly. 'Of course. Loving Andreas makes no difference to my affection for you, Philip. It never has—we've known each other too long.'

He smiled as though she had hurt more than she had pleased, his eyes dark. 'Don't give me back my ring yet.'

Her eyes held surprise and alarm and he closed her fingers over the ring. 'Keep the ring for now, wear it, don't tell anyone the engagement is off.'

'Why?' Bewilderment clouded her expression.

'For your own protection,' he said soberly. 'I don't trust Keralides, I never did. I don't believe this amnesia nonsense—it's too pat. He's a clever swine.'

'Oh, Philip, really! You haven't seen him!'

He smiled wryly. 'Oh, I don't doubt he's really ill after crashing his car, but there's no way you can test amnesia the way you can test a broken leg. He could be pulling the wool over everyone's eyes.'

'Why should he?' Lauren was impatient, incredulous. It was a thought which had visited her once, at the beginning, but now she could not believe that Andreas could be pretending to have lost his memory. It had gone on for too long.

Philip shrugged. 'It worked, didn't it? He got you back.'

Her face flushed. 'If he'd wanted me he would have tried before. You forget, his wife died two years ago and he never came near me after her death. Why should he wait so long?'

'Who the hell knows? He's a devious, cunning businessman and his tactics seem to work.' He stared at her, mouth tight. 'Lauren, you read the papers, you know how many other women have been seen around with him in the past two years. His affairs are notorious. Is that the sort of man you want? A man you can't trust?'

Lauren felt sick, her hands at her stomach, her lips trembling. 'No,' she accepted, her voice a whisper. 'No, of course not.'

'Then why?'

She looked at him helplessly. 'At the moment, he needs me.' At Philip's grimace she said angrily, 'He does! And while he does I can't just turn my back and walk away. I tried at first, I really fought it, but now I can't. I'm weak and stupid, maybe, but I can't do a thing about it.'

There was a silence, then Philip said, 'Very well, I accept that. But for your own protection wear my ring for a time, at least. Wait, Lauren, don't commit yourself to Keralides again until you know just what the position is. Don't lay yourself wide open to any more betrayals from him.'

She knew it made sense, her own intelligence told her so. Slowly she slid the ring back on to her hand. 'You're a wonderful man, Philip,' she said. 'I wish to God I loved you the way you love me.'

He laughed deeply. 'So do I, my dear.'

Unknowingly she gave him a rueful, affectionate smile which held a faint invitation and Philip's eyes darkened.

'You're a very beautiful girl,' he said heavily. 'A pity Keralides wasn't killed in that damned crash.'

She winced. 'Philip! Don't say such a thing, even in a joke.'

'No joke,' he said coolly, and there was tenacity in his stare. 'If you'd never met Keralides, you and I would have been married years ago—I'm certain of that. After you left him I knew you would turn to me sooner or later, Lauren, and you did, and you will again, because as sure as God made little green apples, Keralides will kick you in the teeth again some day, and I'll be here waiting for you.'

He turned and walked out without saying goodbye, and she stood there, shivering, because although half of her resented what he had said about Andreas, the other half suspected it to be true.

The bandages were removed from Andreas's head when she next visited him. She laughed, looking at the tiny black wisps of curls which covered his head. 'You look like a baby!'

'I feel a damned fool.'

He was sitting up against a bank of pillows. That terrible pallor had gone, but after weeks in this room he had lost his habitual golden bronze and was looking as though he needed some weeks in the sun. He had lost weight. The powerful features were even more fleshless, the beautiful dark eyes shadowed.

'Now for the good news,' he said lightly. 'They say I can leave the hospital soon if I take a nurse with me.'

Lauren could not hide the shock which ran through her. He saw her face change, saw the flare of panic and alarm spring into her green eyes.

'What is it?' he asked, staring at her. 'Don't you want me home, Lauren?'

Lauren could feel the distance spreading between them once again. Soon he would have to be told the truth. Once he came out of hospital it could not be kept from him. But not today, she thought, and was furious with her own weakness. If Andreas was strong enough to be sent home, he was strong enough to hear the truth, and her reluctance to tell him was only too revealing.

'Of course I want you home,' she said, smiling far too brightly. 'You must be bored with hospital life.'

'Sick to death with it,' he said grimly, his face taut with a tension she could sense.

He had asked no questions about the lies which Lydia had told him, accepting calmly her story that his father had seen him during the first days after his accident but had been forced to fly to the States since

Andreas recovered. Andreas knew that business came before everything else. She wondered if he had ever asked for Martine. He had not mentioned the girl in her presence, and of course, if he had spoken to his mother about Martine Lydia would never mention it. It was strange, all the same, the way in which Andreas seemed to ignore everything which did not fit in with his belief that this was happening during their first year of marriage. The doctor would say it was subconsciously deliberate, but was it merely subconscious? Did he know what he was doing?

He was talking now about his plans, holding her fingers in one of his hands, playing with them, watching the way they were swallowed up in his larger grip.

'I thought we could go to Greece,' he said, and she suddenly sat upright, her body freezing.

'Greece?' she repeated to gain time, and felt his eyes flash to her face.

'London's so cold in winter and I'm sick for my own skies,' he said quickly. 'The Villa can be opened at a moment's notice. We could fly there as soon as I leave hospital.'

Her heart was thudding fiercely, her lips dry with tension. He had to be told. She could not go to Greece with him; it was out of the question.

'You're very quiet,' said Andreas, a question in his voice.

'I was thinking,' she murmured huskily. 'It would be too much for you. The journey would exhaust you.'

'Nonsense!' he retorted with a return of the old certainty, his face hard with determination. He looked at her and laughter filled his face, a teasing mockery which she remembered only too well and which made her catch her breath and shiver. 'I believe you're shy, Lauren,' he whispered. 'Is it because we've been apart for so long?'

Her eyes searched his quickly. What did he mean?

'Have you forgotten while I've been ill that you're a married woman, and my wife?' he said very softly. 'I'll soon change that, my love. It will be a pleasure to remind you that you belong to me.'

Panic made her try to pull her hand away from him and he tightened his hold on her fingers, shooting a hard look at her averted face.

'I thought these delicious little struggles were over,' he said almost with menace, watching her. 'I see they're not.' He lifted her trapped hand and turned it over, palm upwards, bending his black head to kiss the warm pink skin, his mouth travelling tantalisingly up to the wrist and lingering there, brushing her pulsing vein again and again.

Lauren's heart hammered against her breastbone as she watched him, hating and loving at once, her green eyes wide with frantic emotion. He looked up and she hurriedly dropped her lashes over her eyes, afraid of letting him see precisely what effect he had had on her.

Surely the doctors would not agree to let him fly to Greece? she thought. The journey would be an ordeal for him in his present condition, and he would be so far removed from medical supervision on the island. There was a doctor there, of course, but he was old and certainly not equipped to deal with a serious case.

'Perhaps later we could go to Greece,' she said huskily. 'But not yet, Andreas.'

He gave her a long, cool look from the dark eyes. 'I would recover much faster in my old home.' There was that inexorable fixity of willpower in his features, his jawbone taut, his mouth a straight line.

'I have to go,' she said, pulling away. She ran to the door and his eyes followed her, narrowing, their darkness lit with anger.

'Come back, Lauren!' he said sharply, but she ran out, pretending not to hear, her body trembling.

She went to see Lydia straight from the hospital. The Keralides house was in a quiet, exclusive area near Regent's Park, in an elegant white stuccoed terrace which curved gently behind wrought iron railings, the buildings showing no signs of their century and a half of occupation.

A butler admitted her. He knew her, of course. He had worked for the family for ten years. But there was no sign of anything human on his calm façade. Bowing her into the morning room, he announced her to Lydia with an expressionless voice. 'Miss Grey, madam.'

Lydia got up and came to kiss her, bracelets jangling on her arms. 'Darling, how wonderful to see you in this house again!' She had not visited the house since the night she left it five years ago.

She brushed her cheek against Lydia's and groaned. 'Lydia, do you know that the doctors say he can leave the hospital soon?'

Lydia smiled, eyes gentle. 'Yes. Will you take coffee?' She rang and the butler reappeared. 'Sit down, darling,' Lydia said as he vanished with his orders.

Lauren looked at her desperately. 'Listen to me, Lydia. He wants to go to Greece.'

'What a good idea! I'm sure he will recover twice as fast there.' Lydia seemed unmoved and it was obvious that she had not yet seen the implications.

'Once he's home he must be told, Lydia,' said Lauren, staring at her, her face determined.

'Told what?' Lydia settled herself on the chair beside her and looked innocently at her.

'You know what I mean! He must be told about the divorce!'

Lydia took her hand, touched the wedding ring she still wore, having completely forgotten to take it off when she left the hospital. 'Why?'

Lauren stared. 'You know very well why! I can't go on with this, Lydia. I'm not his wife and sooner or later he has to know that.'

'Of course, sooner or later,' Lydia said softly. 'But not now, Lauren. Not yet.'

Lauren was aghast, staring at her. 'Can't you see that the situation is impossible for me? I'm at the end of my tether—pretending all day, going there, seeing him, lying to him!'

'You're keeping him happy,' Lydia said. 'My dear, it would be so much safer to let him recover his memory by himself, don't you see? Now that he is stronger it can't be long.' Her face saddened. 'It isn't easy for me, either, you know, remembering to pretend Giorgios is still alive, talking about him as if he were. I loved my husband dearly and it hurts, but I love my son, too, and he must not be upset while he is still weak.'

'But I can't go to Greece!' Lauren burst out hoarsely. 'I can't, Lydia! I'm not his wife. We're not married! How could I fly to Greece with him, live under the same roof?'

Lydia smiled a little teasingly. 'Come, my dear, what harm could there be in that? You are not pretending, are you, that Andreas is well enough to want you to share his bed?'

Colour flooded into Lauren's face. Faintly she whispered, 'And if he did?'

'He couldn't,' Lydia laughed. 'Are you forgetting how ill he is still? Such thoughts will not enter his head for weeks, my dear, and by then he is bound to have recovered his memory.'

Lauren took a deep breath, her panic subsiding a little, glancing away before Lydia could read her expression.

'You need a holiday, too,' Lydia said complacently. 'It has all been a strain, I know.' She searched Lauren's pale face closely. 'You look tired, my dear.'

'I couldn't,' said Lauren, but her voice held no conviction.

'You think your fiancé might object?' Lydia watched her as she spoke.

Lauren's blank look betrayed her and her colour rose as she met the amusement in her mother-in-law's dark eyes. Half angrily she rose, just as the butler brought in the great silver tray.

'Coffee,' Lydia said softly, her hand around Lauren's wrist, smiling at her. 'Sit down again, my dear.'

When they were alone again Lauren sipped her coffee without knowing what she was doing, unaware of the excellent taste. Her eyes were feverishly bright as she looked at Lydia.

'When Andreas does recover his memory what's he going to think? It will look as if . . .' She broke off, not daring to say what was in her mind. Andreas might imagine she had leapt at the chance to be with him again, and that stung. She could not tolerate the thought that he might raise those black brows in sardonic amusement at the idea that she had wanted to pretend to be his wife once more.

'I will tell him that I begged you to pretend,' Lydia said very softly, watching her.

'You think he'll believe that?' Lauren's teeth came together fiercely, her cheeks flaming. 'He knows me better.'

'But you did it for me,' Lydia murmured in a gentle voice. 'Didn't you, Lauren?'

Lauren met the faint smile in the dark eyes with a groan of self-contempt. 'At first,' she said harshly.

'And later?' Lydia looked at her mildly, but there was satisfaction in her eyes.

Lauren put down her cup and covered her face with her trembling hands. Before Lydia could move to comfort her she had sprung up, though, moving away across the room to stand with her back to the other woman, her head bent.

'You seem to forget how much reason I have to hate him! Ours was hardly some civilised, amicable separation.'

Lydia's face changed, hardened. 'I do not want to discuss what happened, Lauren. Marriage is a very private affair.'

Lauren laughed scornfully, turning to stare at her, hands clenched at her sides. 'Divorce isn't a bit private, though, is it? You know exactly why I divorced him.'

'Lauren, please!'

Lauren was too angry to stop now. Face white, she said bitterly, 'It happened here in this house, remember. I walked in and saw them in bed together.'

Lydia flinched, her mouth compressed and pale. 'I'm sorry I....'

'Sorry?' Lauren threw the word at her as if it had been an insult. 'Can you imagine what it was like for me?' Her voice held ragged pain and anger and her face was taut with the attempt to control the misery burning inside her.

'Oh, my dear,' Lydia murmured, sighing deeply.

'Could you just forget it, if you were me?' The question was flung at her like a dagger, sharp and cold.

'You have never allowed Andreas to explain,' Lydia said in husky tones.

'Explain? What, for God's sake? What could he explain, Lydia? Why he took Martine to my bed that night? I saw them, remember. I've had that picture to live with ever since, and it put me through hell, believe me. No amount of excuses could make up for that.'

'Things are never as simple as they seem,' Lydia protested in a shaky, distressed voice, looking at her with dark eyes which held anxious sadness.

Lauren laughed bitterly. 'That was very simple, Lydia. That was as plain as a pikestaff.'

Lydia's eyes held wincing pain. 'Don't talk like that! I hate to hear you.'

'I don't exactly love it myself,' said Lauren, lip curling. 'But I won't listen to you playing devil's advocate to Andreas. Nothing he could say would remove Niko from the scene, Lydia, nor, I think, would you want it to. I realise you love the boy, and I've no doubt he's a nice little boy, but every time I hear his name I'm reminded of the fact that Andreas is his father and that he was conceived that night in my bedroom.'

She walked to the door and went out, leaving Lydia staring after her with a tragic face.

CHAPTER FOUR

'He's shamming,' Jimmy said flatly, staring at her. 'He must be. Lauren, you can't even consider going to Greece with him. It's taken you years to get over the last disaster. Only a fool goes back for more punishment.' His mouth twisted. 'Or a masochist. Is that what you are, Lauren? Did you actually enjoy the treatment he meted out to you last time?'

Her face white, her eyes enormous, she shook her head. 'Of course not!'

'Then why? Why let it all happen again?'

She wrung her hands together in a helpless gesture. 'I never intended to let it go so far. The first time Lydia more or less dragged me there and then I thought he was dying.' She swallowed, remembering that day with a sensation of cold misery. 'How could I refuse, Jimmy? When he might be dying.'

Her father clicked his tongue, pushing a hand through his untidy thin hair. 'Well, he isn't dying now, far from it, and if he's strong enough to go to Greece he's strong enough to hear the truth.'

She couldn't deny it. Bending her head, she sighed. 'Lydia wants him to recover his memory naturally.'

Jimmy's expression was ironic. 'No matter how long it takes? Do they intend to keep all newspapers from him? Business matters? For God's sake, Lauren, can't you see what I'm getting at? He has to know, he just has to be shamming. Otherwise, wouldn't he ask questions?'

Lauren's eyes opened wide. 'Newspapers? But I've been reading them to him when I visited him.'

Her father grinned sardonically. 'Yes? And he never once commented on what you read? Showed no surprise? Although in five years so much has changed in the world?'

She sat down as if her legs would no longer support her. 'I see what you mean. That never occurred to me.'

'One glance at a newspaper date would open his eyes,' said Jimmy. 'Do you think he wouldn't ask someone about what appeared to be a gap of five years in his memory?' He looked at her gently. 'Darling, don't you realise how much you've changed in five years? The last time he saw you, you were a young girl. Now you're a woman. Even the way you wear your hair, your make-up, your clothes. They would all be strange to him. Yet he never once remarked on it. Can you believe that?'

Jimmy's shrewd, penetrating intelligence had always been quicker than her own. He went right to the heart of a problem, undeterred by the irrelevancies which often cluttered her own vision. With one leap he had done so now, seeing at once the inconsistencies which she should have seen but which her troubled involvement with Andreas had hidden from her. Of course, he was right: Andreas could scarcely have spent the last six weeks without having once questioned, remarked upon the gap in his memory. When she first saw Lydia she had seen at once the alteration in her appearance in five years, yet Andreas had said nothing of it.

Her green eyes very wide, she asked faintly, 'Why can he be doing it?'

'Why?' Jimmy's mouth tightened. 'You aren't that blind, Lauren. You know as well as I do why he's doing it. He wants you back.'

Her face flushed deeply and her heart missed a beat. Raggedly, she said: 'He still loves me?' And stared at her father, waiting for his reply, with bated breath.

Jimmy surveyed her grimly. 'Loves? Not the word I would have used. Wants, Lauren. He's a possessive man, very aware of his power. You got away from him. It surprised me at the time that he let you go so easily, with only a token fight. The day he came here after you he was like a maniac. It took both Philip and me to throw him out. One thing stuck in my mind at the time—the way he said: "She's mine." It sent a shiver down my back. I've no time for men like that, men who see women as possessions.'

His words brought back the piercing, bitter flood of remembered jealousy and pain and she was unable to speak or move for a moment, staring down at the floor, eyes fixed in agony.

When her throat eased enough for her to be confident of speaking, she asked huskily, 'What am I going to do?'

Her father had brought her up after her mother's death. They were very close. Lauren had inherited his talent, his intelligence, his passion for beauty. He had taught her to see it in the most unlikely objects, opening her eyes to life with tolerant humanity, giving her a basis of calm philosophy on which to build her own view of life. She had not suspected for a long time that the succession of beautiful if frequently dull models who passed through their lives had anything but a business relationship with him, but when it did become clear to her that her father liked women, she was old enough to accept it without despising him, as she had accepted Emma, the girl he had brought back with him from Spain, a very small, frank American with rich auburn hair and a wide smile. At least she could cook, Lauren thought, her eyes amused, and although she was at least half Jimmy's age she had a calm sincerity which had made her instantly likeable.

The casual relationships which Jimmy formed had given her a sense of emptiness, however, which had formed her attitude towards Andreas. She had wanted him all to herself in those early days. His family had been a bone of contention between them, since Lauren was unable to accept the close-woven pattern of family life as the Keralides knew it. She had been hungry for permanence, for possession of every corner of her husband's heart, which made her resentful of any other demand on him.

'Do?' Jimmy answered her at last. 'You must do as you please, Lauren, but Andreas is playing out a charade, you know, and if you go on seeing him you're going to get hurt all over again.'

Was Andreas pretending? she asked herself, when he had gone, or was he merely blanking out certain memories because he preferred not to remember them?

It was possible, she admitted reluctantly, that he was hoping that he could wipe out the past. He might believe that if he could get her to see him often enough she would gradually forget what had happened. And it was coming true, she thought, wincing. She had to remind herself now. Anger with Andreas shot up like mercury inside her. If he was pretending, he was a devious, lying swine, she thought furiously.

She told herself a hundred times that day that she would not visit him, she would stay away from now on, tell Lydia that the game was over. But in the end she went, deriding herself for her weak-mindedness, arguing with herself every inch of the way. Even as she stood outside his room she hesitated. She was several hours past the time she usually came. She still had a chance to turn round and walk away.

Then, as she stood there, she heard a strange sound within the room, a muffled groan. He was in pain. At once she opened the door, her eyes flying towards the bed, and saw his dark head, the curls thicker and more lustrous every day as they grew, buried in the pillow. He did not move, his face hidden from her, and she ran across the room to him, touching his shoulder, whispering, 'Andreas? What is it?'

He lay still for a moment, then, face still buried, he whispered unsteadily, 'Nothing. My head. . . .'

She sat down, stroking the short curls, massaging his nape. 'It hurts? Shall I get the nurse? How bad is it?'

'Better now,' he sighed, and she felt the muscles in his neck relax under her caressing fingers. 'Keep doing that.' Her fingers burrowed under the black hair, pressing gently into his scalp, and he breathed deeply. 'Ah, that's so good! You have healing hands, Lauren.'

For a moment longer she sat there, tenderly massaging his head, then she drew her hand away, a flush mounting to her cheeks as she realised just what she was doing, how she was feeling. All her hard intention had vanished. How could she confront him after this?

He lay there a moment longer, then turned on to his back, his eyes lifting to her face. 'You're late,' he said. 'I thought you weren't coming.'

She looked down, lashes flickering against her cheek. 'I was working.'

'Painting?' He asked the question slowly and she looked up at him to search his expression, but he looked calm, unconcerned, the dark eyes impossible to read. If he was acting he had to be doing so superbly. What if Jimmy and Philip were wrong? What if it were not a charade he was playing out for his own reasons? Could she, dared she, force his memory and shock him into some sort of collapse? Could she live with herself if she harmed him in any way?

He looked down and his fingers pleated the white bedcover. He seemed to concentrate on it, his face unreadable. 'Are you seeing much of Colby?'

Lauren drew in her breath sharply and he looked up, eyes penetrating. 'I see him now and then,' she said, staring back at him, trying to read his mind.

He looked away without answering her. His face was tired, pale, and her heart moved inside her as she watched the weary lines of it. 'You're tired. I'd better go and let you sleep,' she said.

He put his hand out, taking hers, holding it tightly. 'Stay,' he said, and it was not a plea, it was a command; his voice held harshness.

'Mama has made all the arrangements for Greece,' he said suddenly as they sat there in silence.

Her hand jerked within his and she felt him looking up at her, felt his fingers tighten around her own.

'Andreas,' she said huskily, opening her mouth to tell him now, because she could not go to Greece, she could not go on with this pretence.

'The nurse will be with us, you don't need to worry in case the journey proves difficult for me,' he said, breaking in on her words. 'I expect they will drug me to the eyeballs, anyway. They don't seem keen for me to go, but I've had enough of this room. I want to get out of this hospital atmosphere, relax in my own surroundings.' He sighed heavily. 'I'm so sick of hospital life, Lauren. Six weeks is long enough. I'm certain that I'll get back to normal quicker in Greece than anywhere else.'

'Is the nurse one of those who've been looking after you?' she asked, more to gain time while she thought than because she was really interested.

He laughed abruptly. 'No, they got in an outside agency. The girl came here this morning to talk it over with my doctors.' His dark eyes glinted provocatively at her, a smile on his mouth. 'Wait until you see her! I never knew nurses could look like that.'

'Like what?' she asked, and there was no sense in hiding it from herself, she was jealous at once, she felt the familiar flick of it in her stomach.

'A pure redhead,' he said, grinning. 'With a figure like a film star's. I'll have to watch my pulse readings with her around.'

Her eyes shone bright, dangerous green and he looked amused, his eyes flickering over her angry face. But in a strange way, this teasing lightened her mood, for surely if he remembered the past he would not taunt her like that, deliberately, because it had been quite deliberate, the triumphant enjoyment in his eyes told her as much, and in the beginning he had sometimes teased her in just such a fashion, liking to see her fly into a rage at his provocative remarks. She could not believe he would do so now if he remembered Martine, their divorce. It was too painful for him to joke about such things. He would have known he was treading into a minefield by hinting at possible infidelity.

When she left him ten minutes later no more had been said about the trip to Greece, but she knew she was weakening, tempted by the idea of being alone with him at the villa there. She walked for an hour in cold, freezing weather, her thoughts too tangled for her to be able to unravel them honestly, watching the London streets with an absent eye which passed over shops, pedestrians, cars and double-decker red buses and never saw them.

She stood by the fountains in Trafalgar Square and faced facts grimly. She wanted to go. Andreas was offering her a mixture of heaven and hell, but she was very tempted to accept it, because his amnesia was a face-saving excuse for doing just what she wanted to do. These weeks had shown her only too clearly that his absence hurt more than his past cruelty to her. Pride might dictate that she get out of his life and never see him again, but hungry, obsessive love demanded the opposite.

In the first, wounded, jealous rage of discovering him with Martine, she had wanted to hit back at him by taking a lover herself, to show him she did not care, to soothe the knife-wound in her own flesh with an act of revenge.

It had been a crazy impulse. Only her own innate sense of pride had deterred her from some wild act. Once or twice, indeed, she had gone as far as flirting with some casually met stranger, but each time she had retreated before the flirtation became anything more.

She might have given herself to Philip if she had been seeing him, but on her father's advice she had stayed away from London for months while her divorce went through, and by the time she did come back she had rediscovered her equilibrium, sufficient, anyway, to have withdrawn again behind a cloak of cool control. She had sunk herself in work, studying feverishly in an effort to forget everything else.

The night she heard of Andreas's marriage to Martine she went to a party and met an attractive young man who came back to her apartment when the party ended. She almost slept with him, but at the last moment could not bring herself to do it.

The memory of sensual pleasure in Andreas's arms had receded painfully. When she turned to Philip she had not expected even a dim shadow of the passion she had once known; unable, in fact, to offer it to him however she tried. Her affection for him had been deep and loving, but it had been lukewarm compared with the fierce engagement of the senses which she had achieved with Andreas.

It came back, in the end, to a clear-cut decision as to whether she believed that Andreas had lost his memory and whether, in that case, she could bear to spend a few weeks with him in Greece under such circumstances.

She went to his mother's house, at last, and Lydia sat beside her, holding her hand, listening quietly while she tried to explain her complex emotions.

Gently, Lydia said, 'You make it all too complicated, my dear. There is only one question for you to answer to yourself. Do you want to go with him?'

Lauren groaned. 'You know very well I do.'

She saw the satisfaction in the dark eyes but she could not even feel angry with Lydia, she was too disturbed and troubled by her own emotions. She had no time to worry about those of other people. Lydia had never made any secret of her desire to get them back together again. Two years ago she had rung Lauren out of the blue to tell her that Martine had been drowned in Greece and Andreas was free again. Lauren, stung beyond caring, had sharply said she couldn't care less, slamming down the phone. Lydia had rung again, undeterred by this initial rebuff. 'Andreas would jump at the chance to see you again,' she had said. 'It could be a casual meeting, you could come to lunch with me here.' Lauren had bitten her head off again and imagined that that would be the end of it, but Lydia had proved more persistent than that. Only after a number of angry refusals had the calls stopped.

She looked at her now, frowning. 'Lydia, two years ago when you rang me after Martine died, did Andreas know you were calling me?'

Lydia visibly hesitated. Lauren could read the desire

to lie in her dark eyes as she fumbled for words, then she sighed, shaking her head. 'No, he did not know.'

Lauren felt herself sagging like a collapsed balloon.

'He wanted to see you again,' Lydia went on hurriedly. 'I knew that. You wouldn't dispute that I do know Andreas better than anyone in the world does, would you, Lauren? He had you permanently on his mind. There were a hundred little pointers to it, but he was afraid. Afraid you would refuse in such a way that it would scar him even more.'

Lauren's temper flared. 'Scar him? What scars has he got? You sound sometimes as though he was in need of sympathy from me, but what happened was his doing, not mine. Scarred? I'd like to see him burning in hell, Lydia. I hate him!'

Silently, Lydia looked at her and shook her head, implying that she did not believe a word of it, and already Lauren was subsiding again into weary despair, sick of herself, sick of Andreas, sick of everything.

'It all seemed cut and dried a month or two ago,' she said in a dry voice. 'I hated him. I could have stepped over him in a gutter if he was bleeding to death and never stopped to look. These last weeks have undermined me and I sometimes suspect he's done it all deliberately, I begin to doubt he has lost his memory, I think he's playing some elaborate game with me.'

Lydia watched her, her face softly obstinate, the thin lines filled with that passive immovability which was such a strength to her.

'And if he were? Would you understand?'

Lauren stiffened. Was she admitting it? She stared at her. 'Is he?'

'The doctors say not,' Lydia said flatly. 'They are sure he genuinely has blocked out all that memory of the past, but that aside, Lauren, if he had been pretending, could you understand his need to cloak himself before he approached you, for his pride's sake? Andreas is a true Keralides. His pride is massive—it always has been. It would be a failure in his masculinity for him to admit any weakness, particularly before a woman. Might he not be pardoned for that?'

'He trampled on my pride,' said Lauren. 'Why should I forgive him for protecting his own?'

Lydia gestured with her thin shoulders, hands spread wide. 'A woman's pride is expendable, we both know that. We have never put so much emphasis on it, have we? It is men who treasure it, fight for it, are prepared to die for it. A woman has more practical common sense than to sacrifice so much as a hair for pride.'

'You're talking about Greeks,' said Lauren, faintly smiling. 'An Englishman doesn't talk of dying for pride's sake, believe me.'

Lydia looked politely scornful, dark eyes bright. 'An Englishman! We talk of Andreas, your husband and my son.'

Flushing, Lauren shook her head. 'He's no longer my husband.'

'Not in your heart?' Lydia asked gently.

'When I saw him with Martine he killed my heart,' Lauren said with a trace of Lydia's own dramatic language. 'For a while, anyway, I was as empty as death and when I came out of that I'd learnt better than to give my heart away ever again. No, Lydia, Andreas is not my husband in any sense of the word.'

'Then why are you tempted to go to Greece with him?' Lydia was triumphant as she asked that and Lauren felt herself flush hotly.

She jumped to her feet. 'I'm a fool,' she said harshly. 'I must be, or I wouldn't even consider it.'

'But you will go,' Lydia said wisely, smiling. 'Won't you, Lauren?'

Lauren could not answer, standing in the room with clenched fists and a face torn between conflicting emotions.

After a long moment she said, 'If I go, I want no redheaded nurse, Lydia.'

Lydia's eyes opened wide. 'What?'

'The nurse they sent along from this agency, Andreas claims she's a raving beauty.' She was being childishly blatant in her jealousy and it soothed her to be so; she stared at Lydia with her lip stuck out in a babyish pout. 'Change her. Get someone older. I will not have Andreas teasing me with her while we're there!'

Lydia laughed delightedly. 'Did he?'

'Oh, quite deliberately, he made no pretence of it being anything but a tease, but I won't have it.'

Lydia's eyes sparkled. 'I'll get a dragon, I promise.'

'As ugly as sin, preferably,' Lauren said in a high voice. 'Let me see him flirt with her!'

'I'll choose the oldest, ugliest nurse they have on their books,' Lydia swore, laughing. And as she walked to the door with Lauren later she said softly, 'And you pretend to be indifferent to him!'

Lauren grimaced. 'Indifferent? I wish I was, but it doesn't mean I've forgiven him. I never will.'

Four days later she flew to Greece with Andreas in the private plane owned by the Keralides empire and the nurse who accompanied them was a woman of fifty, her comfortable body sheathed in her dark blue uniform, her practical, commonsense shoes planted firmly on the ground as she saw to the patient.

Andreas eyed Lauren wryly as the nurse retired to her own seat. 'I have you to thank for my gorgon, I gather. Or was Mama making that up?'

Lauren lifted her chin in defiance. 'I don't know what you're talking about,' she lied, and he gave her a peculiar, glittering smile.

'No?'

The plane banked sharply and she gasped, looking out of the window. His hand covered her own. 'No need to worry. We are only turning to enter the flight path.'

She looked down at the fleshless hand covering her own and felt her stomach tighten at the contact. Although she had seen him every day for weeks they had always been in the clinical atmosphere of the hospital, and only now was she beginning to appreciate the difference there would be when they were alone at the Villa.

His hand withdrew as though she had made some comment and he turned his dark head to look out of the window in his turn, his profile hard and unreadable.

After a few moments his lids drooped. The drugs he had been given before take-off began to have their effect. He slowly slid into sleep while she watched him.

He woke during the flight, and ate a light meal without much evidence of appetite, his cheeks glazed with a hot flush, then fell almost at once back into sleep, his head tilting towards her. For the first time she really understood the weakness which still held him captive. Asleep, he looked strangely, movingly vulnerable: the strong dark features relaxed, his mouth softened, his lids covering the dark eyes. Lauren had a burning urge to touch him as she watched him, her fingertips aching for the feel of his skin. It would have been easy to do so without his knowing as his head slid down sideways against her shoulder, but she forced down the impulse, turning her head away.

It was an effort to remember that she hated him. She had to keep reminding herself, whipping herself into an anger which no longer seemed to matter.

From Athens they flew on to the little island of Aelimos, the rocky outline of it invisible in the darkness as they circled before landing, only the few stars of landing lights visible from the plane. The villa lay a quarter of a mile from the landing strip and Andreas sat bolt upright as they drove there, peering out through the black night, renewing memories of this small place which he had known as a home base since he was tiny.

Spiro was driving them, his enormous muscled body solid in the front of the car, talking over his shoulder to Andreas in fluent, fast Greek, telling him all about the news he had missed, the gossip he might care to know.

Lauren dozed, not listening, worn out by the long journey, and her head nodded down towards Andreas as she slept. When the car halted she woke with a start to find herself held close to him, his arm around her shoulders, the warmth of his body under her cheek.

Flushed, she sat up, pushing herself away. Andreas was helped out by Spiro and insisted, sharply and obstinately, on walking into the villa. He walked slowly, resting at every other step, but he made it, and Spiro's broad grin applauded him.

Spiro lived in residence at the villa while it was not used by the family. His wife, Helen, met them, her weathered face alight with smiles and tears, sobbing delighted words as she hugged Andreas uninhibitedly, kissed him on both cheeks again and again.

Both Spiro and Helen had known him since childhood. They had a gruff, forthright way of talking to him, saying what they thought without hesitation, making it clear when they approved or disapproved. Helen's short, stumpy figure was always in black. She had lost her eldest son ten years ago when he was drowned in his fishing boat and she still mourned, still lit candles for him in the little island church. Her other son, Dimitri, grew olives in the mountainous interior of the island, living with his wife and four children in a whitewashed house among his groves, visiting his parents once a week on Sunday. Andreas asked after him and smiled as he listened to Helen's retort, her face filled with the fierce pride and impatience of a woman who often quarrelled with but adored her son.

Lauren stood there, waiting for Helen to notice her, wondering what reaction she would get when the old woman did turn to her. The dark eyes turned her way at last, but Helen showed no surprise at seeing her. She merely held out her arms and, when Lauren obediently went into them, hugged her as she had hugged Andreas, kissing her warmly. As Lauren moved away, her own cheeks wet where the old woman's face had touched her, Helen gave her a look unmistakably filled with approval and pleasure.

'Good, good,' she said in her thick, halting English, before breaking out once more in Greek which she knew Lauren could understand even if she spoke it rather slowly. Lauren had learnt Greek during the first months of her marriage. English had been a barrier between her and the Keralides family, even though they spoke it perfectly, since they liked to lapse cosily into their own tongue when they were en famille, and to have someone among them not understanding was tiresome to them. Lauren had felt excluded by it at first, almost suspecting that they were doing it deliberately, but when she had learnt enough of their tongue to follow their talk she found that the habit was ingrained and they had meant her no particular malice by it.

Andreas was looking white now and the nurse interrupted to ask if he might now go to bed. Clucking, Helen led the way up the stairs. The villa had been built by his grandfather forty years ago and had been little modernised since then, the Keralides preferring to keep it as it had always been, a gracious Victorian villa with large airy rooms, high windows and a dignified aspect which blended charmingly into the island landscape.

Andreas was left to the ministrations of his nurse at last, Helen only retiring grudgingly, her dark-eyed suspicion making it plain that she did not feel easy entrusting her precious nursling to a stranger. Helen's antagonism towards strangers had once included Lauren herself, but she had begun to soften before the divorce and now she seemed eager to make Lauren feel at home, fussing round her gently, offering her food and wine, asking her to ask if there was anything she needed, any way in which Helen could please her. Left alone in her own room at last Lauren faced the fact that Lydia had given Helen and Spiro instructions about her. Their unsurprised welcome made that obvious.

She was too tired tonight to care. She fell asleep the moment her eyes closed and she slept heavily through the long warm night. When she woke it was daylight and she lay listening to the distant sound of the sea breaking on the rocks, watching the wintry sunlight play around the walls, strangely at ease in this isolated, peaceful place. All the tension and strain of the last weeks seemed far away and her heart turned over with a sudden realisation that she and Andreas were together under one roof for the first time in five years.

CHAPTER FIVE

THE journey had been more exhausting than Andreas had wished to admit. For two days after their arrival his nurse insisted that he stay in bed, despite his protests, and her firm stand was vindicated by the fact that, whenever Lauren went in to see him, she found him half asleep, a grey weariness in his hard features. He would stir drowsily, the dark eyes gleaming through his lashes, and smile faintly at her, that trace of sardonic self-mockery on his straight mouth. 'It seems to have knocked me out,' he grimaced the first time. 'Sorry, Lauren.' And she stood by the bed, smiling at him, her fingers gently pushing the soft black hair back from his forehead. 'It doesn't matter. You'll soon get your strength back.'

While he rested, she made her way around the villa gardens in a pilgrimage of remembrance, each new sight reminding her sharply of moments in the past. The vision of herself six years ago was painful. From the vantage point of today she could see how young she had been, an inexperienced eighteen-year-old with no idea what manner of man she had captured; uncertain of him and herself, over-sensitive, easily hurt. She had been wide open to the wound Martine had made, an easy target. No wonder the Greek girl had laughed at her!

During the visits she and Andreas had made to the

villa during their marriage they had spent hours on the
little private beach below the house. Andreas loved to
lie in the sun relaxing totally. Teasingly she had once
told him he had lizard blood, reminded by the motion-
less geckos which haunted the villa grounds by night,
sometimes clinging to the windows, their bulging little
eyes watching for insects. The island was over run with
lizards, they sunbathed on every rock, drinking in the
sun through every scale. Now, in winter, they were
hibernating down among the rocks and the sea had a
glittering coldness which did not attract. Walking on
the beach she never met a soul, only saw the sea birds
wheel and cry out over the white-topped waves.

On the third morning Andreas was well enough recovered to make a stand against his nurse, insisting
that he could get up. She would have kept him in bed
for a few days longer if she could, but his autocratic
manner cowed her now that he was himself again.
Dark eyes furious, he barked, 'I am getting up!'
Lauren was in her room when she heard his voice and
turned to listen, a half-smile on her face. That was the
Andreas she remembered. She had not heard that note
in his voice since the accident.

Eyeing herself in her mirror she was in two minds
about the clothes she had chosen to wear that morning. The silky sea-green blouse was pretty enough, but
Andreas disliked seeing her in trousers. He was bound
to frown at the black ones she was wearing. Her eyes
flashed as she realised the way her thoughts were tend-
ing. He had no right to dictate what she wore! What
was she thinking about? She stiffened and drew away

from the mirror, head high. She would not dress to please *him*.

She tapped at his door and the nurse came to admit her, looking ruffled, her broad face flushed. 'He's playing up, Mrs Keralides,' she whispered crossly, as though Andreas were a naughty boy who needed a good slap, which, Lauren thought wryly, he did, and she would love to give him one. If she dared.

Andreas was sitting up against his banked pillows, his arms folded across his silk pyjamas, his eyes glittering. 'Why all the whispering?' he demanded, glaring across the room. 'Lauren, come here! I'll have no conspiracies behind my back.'

She gave the nurse a rueful smile, half apologetic, then crossed the room with his dark eyes on her at every step, angrily aware of the narrowed interest with which he surveyed her and feeling even more that she would like to slap him. His glance slid from her smoothly pleated blonde hair to her small, high breasts under the greenish silk and then with a quirk of his hard mouth to the black trousers.

'Why are you wearing those things?' he asked impatiently. 'I hate women in trousers. Take them off.'

She looked coolly at him, one eyebrow lifted. 'We're irritable this morning, aren't we, nurse?'

'We always are when we're feeling a bit better,' the nurse said comfortably, and Andreas gave them both an infuriated look.

'Don't talk about me as if I were a child, for God's sake. I won't stand for it!'

'You'll have to lie down for it, then,' Lauren said sweetly, enjoying the frustrated rage in his dark eyes.

'You're far too weak to get up today.'

'Lauren, I'm getting up,' he said through his teeth.

She shook her head, smiling very patiently, knowing that nothing would madden him more. 'No, darling. You must do as nurse says.'

He ground his teeth, the bones pushing through his fleshless cheeks.

The nurse, who had been intimidated by his manner, looked delighted, nodding at him complacently. 'Your wife is right, Mr Keralides.'

'Nurse knows best,' Lauren told him so softly that for a moment he looked beside himself, his hands curled into fists on the bedcovers.

'God in heaven!' he muttered, then turned on to his side and lay facing away from them, the whole attitude of his body indicating sullen temper.

The nurse winked at Lauren and stole out. She stood watching the dark head, seeing the tension in the neck muscles beneath the short curling black hair.

'Are you going to sulk all day?'

He turned at that. 'Who's sulking?'

'Oh, Andreas,' she mocked, eyes derisive.

He had the grace to look self-conscious. 'I'm sick of being tied down in bed.' He lowered his lids, the black lashes flickering on his hard cheek. 'I thought we could spend a few hours together.'

Something in the way he said that made her tauten, moving back a step, a pulse leaping behind her wrists. Somehow managing to sound cool, she said, 'You're still ill, Andreas. I know it's hard for you, but you have to face that fact. The journey here was more of an effort than you will admit. Give yourself time to recover from it.'

He lay watching her through his lashes. 'Stay with me, then,' he said, and his tone was more of an invitation than the words implied. She felt her skin heating and glanced away, struggling for composure.

'If I stay you won't rest. You'll talk. You have to learn to relax, Andreas. Just spend a few days doing absolutely nothing.'

'Sounds hellishly boring,' he muttered, the lines of his mouth discontented.

'All the same, it's what you must do,' she said, turning and walking back to the door.

'Where are you going?' He sat up at once, eyes flashing, his dark head as arrogant as that of an emperor on a Roman coin.

'For a walk, I think,' she shrugged. 'I'll see you later.'

'Come back, Lauren!' he snapped, but she ignored him, closing the door. The nurse smiled at her gratefully and Lauren said,

'Keep an eye on him, nurse, or he'll try to escape.'

'Don't worry, Mrs Keralides, I will,' the nurse promised, smoothing down her apron, and something in her voice made Lauren grin.

Feeling gleefully triumphant, she went out of the villa and walked down through the terraced garden to the sea. There was a stiff wind blowing. It whipped her hair into disarray, blew pink colour into her cheeks. It had given her great pleasure to force Andreas to obey her. His physical weakness made him vulnerable, and that was very satisfying. It made her feel able to cope with him. She had no illusions as to the reversal which would take place once he was fit again. He was a man accustomed to command, spoilt by years of wealth and power. Although he had indulged and petted her during the first months of their marriage she had always been in a state of mental slavery, never allowed to lose sight of the fact that Andreas was her superior, in every sense of the word. He had dominated her casually, making her feel that he despised her even when he loved her passionately, as though she were a silk-skinned little alleycat he had picked up and taken home.

She had never been his equal in anything. Even in bed he retained that hidden amusement, as though the sensual pleasure she gave him was delightful yet not essential to him. He had enjoyed teaching her to make love, but he had never lost his head over her, she thought, staring out across the sea. The blue-grey waters stretched to a flat white horizon, the clear, cold light dazzling even in winter. Now, she suspected, no, she knew that Andreas had never taken her seriously, perhaps because she was of a different race. It was galling to admit it to herself. She had been a pretty toy he had bought but of which he had tired in the end, turning instead to Martine, who shared his blood and his racial inheritance, and who, being a Keralides too, could meet him on the same ground.

She quite deliberately kept away from Andreas for the rest of the day, although he sent a message through Helen that he wished to see her. Helen's shrewd dark eyes saw Lauren's tightened mouth as she listened. Lauren politely thanked her and turned away and Helen watched her with unrevealing curiosity.

She went to bed early, assured by the nurse that Andreas had been given a sleeping pill and was already fast asleep. Her prolonged walks around the beach and villa had tired her, and she fell asleep herself almost at once, the light duck-feather duvet making her as cosy as if she slept in a snow drift.

Next morning Andreas was reading a Greek newspaper when she walked into his room. The dark eyes surveyed her as coolly as she looked at him, and she knew that he had changed his attitude since the previous day.

'You look much better,' she observed, walking to the window and glancing out as though fascinated by the pale blue of the sky. 'The weather is better, too. That wind has dropped and it feels quite mild.'

'Come here,' Andreas said, and there was menace in the soft tone.

'I think I'll walk a little way along the cliffs today,' Lauren said, pretending not to have heard.

'Come here or I'll come and get you,' Andreas told her, his dark eyes narrowed in an unspoken threat.

She turned, pretending surprise. 'What's wrong? Feeling cross again? Nurse says it's a mark of convalescence. You'll pull out of it.'

His lips curled back from his white teeth in a savage snarl. 'My God, you're asking for it,' he muttered, and suddenly she was very still, staring at him, a curious stirring in her brain. 'Come here,' he said, extending his hand with a peremptory movement.

She walked to the bed, staring at him, eyes searching. Had she imagined it or had she seen the old Andreas in his face, a hard, antagonistic force which did not accord with his vulnerability since his illness? 'Don't talk to me like that, Andreas,' she said softly, and there was coldness in her oval face. His eyes probed hers, narrowed, then his hand caught her, dragged her down on to the bed, holding her so that she could not escape except by struggling violently and hurting him.

'Let me go!' she exclaimed, twisting to avoid the hard mouth as it travelled across her cheek in search of her lips.

He didn't answer, still trying to make her give him her mouth, but she felt the anger in him, heard it in his indrawn breath, the fierce movement of his hands on her. He jerked her round, despite her struggle, and as she glared at him she knew.

'You ... remember!' she breathed with a shake in her voice.

He gave her a grim little smile, saying nothing, and her own anger flared to meet his, a burning bitter rage which rushed through her like flame through dry brushwood and showed in her green eyes.

Andreas, still saying nothing, put his head down before she had time to burst out with the words which were on her tongue, and his mouth crushed hers, hurting, possessing; a kiss without tenderness or caring, only making clear a rage to force submission from her. She put her hands against his shoulders, fighting to get free, refusing to yield to the power of his mouth, and at last he allowed her to pull away. Breathing very fast, trembling, she looked at his sardonic eyes.

'When did you remember?'

'After your second visit to the hospital,' he said coolly, and that took her breath away. She stayed still, incredulous, staring at him, her face whitened with shock.

'You lying swine,' she whispered hoarsely, then she struggled to get up from the bed. 'Let me go! I'm not staying here now. I'm going.'

'Swimming, are you?' he asked softly, the dark eyes mocking her.

Oh, God, she thought. Of course. How was she to get away? 'I'll find a fishing boat to take me,' she said wildly, and he lifted one derisive dark eyebrow.

'You really think so?'

There wasn't a man on the island who would be prepared to risk Andreas Keralides' wrath by taking her away and they both knew it. Lauren's temper rose as she contemplated the position in which she found herself. She had walked into this trap with her eyes wide open, but it was infuriating, nonetheless.

She looked at him with bitterness. 'Why have you gone on lying all these weeks?'

A barbed mockery sprang into his eyes. 'You mean it never once crossed your mind that I had remembered everything?'

She felt herself flushing but snapped back, 'Of course it occurred to me.'

'Then?' He raised a lazy eyebrow.

'I couldn't believe you would be such a swine,' she retorted. 'I should have known, I suppose, it fitted the pattern, but I still find it hard to believe people can behave with such total lack of scruple.'

That hit the target, she saw. Andreas's dark eyes were volcanic, his jawline taut, but he went on smiling lazily, as though her words were water off a duck's back, and when she tried to pull out of his arms they tightened, retaining her. 'No, you don't,' he said very, very softly, and there was that undertone of menace again.

'I can't stand it when you touch me,' she said fiercely, looking into his face with contempt.

His lids flickered briefly, but he went on smiling and the pressure of his hands against her back was harder. She could feel him exert force, could feel a desire to hurt beneath that smiling mask.

'You can't keep me here against my will,' she flung, wishing she believed what she was saying.

'Can't I?'

'I'll find a way to get off the island!'

He laughed, amusement sparkling in the dark eyes. 'As I said, you can always swim. I hope your swimming has improved. The last time I saw you in the sea you splashed like a dog and could just about do a swimming pool length.'

Lauren was too angry to speak. She looked away and fought for control. After a moment she said, 'All right, you can keep me here, but you can't make me see you.'

He made a little Greek sound, deep in his throat, a noise compounded of derision and dismissal. 'No? And after you've been so kind and loving all these weeks, Lauren! I've thoroughly enjoyed having you dance attendance on me day after day. So sweet and compliant, I barely recognised you, I thought you had really changed your skin.'

'You were wrong.'

'So it seems. A pity. I liked the demure act, you really had me fooled.'

'I had you fooled! Of all the nerve!'

'You should have been an actress,' he said, ignoring her.

'I'm not in your class, Andreas,' she snapped back. 'You acted superbly. I really felt sorry for you. You convinced me and Mama you were dying.' Then her eyes sharpened. 'But did you? Was Lydia in it? Did she know it was all fraud? I suppose she did.'

She sensed that he hesitated and knew he was debating whether to lie or not, but their eyes met and held and the answer was in his face.

She felt a pang of unreasonable pain. Lydia had lied to her too. That hurt. 'My God, I'd never have believed it of her,' she said dazedly. 'How could she do that to me?'

His hands fell away, leaving her free. 'She did it for me,' he said coolly. 'If you must blame someone, blame me. I asked her not to tell you I'd recovered my memory. She was with me when things began to come back. She would have told you if I hadn't begged her not to.' He looked away towards the window, the angle of jaw and cheekbone hard and taut, and Lauren stared at him, swallowing.

'Why?' she asked, despising herself for asking. 'Why did you want to keep it a secret from me? Why go on with this charade day after day?'

Andreas lifted his broad shoulders in a shrug. 'I told you, I was enjoying things as they were.'

'Having me dance attendance, you said,' she muttered furiously, colouring in humiliation. 'You made a fool of me. So did Lydia. She always has spoilt you.'

'Me?' He laughed tightly. 'You're the one who was spoilt, Lauren.'

Incredulous, she stared at his averted profile. 'What on earth do you mean?'

'Your father let you run wild,' he said through his teeth, and his head swung towards her, his dark eyes freezingly cold. 'You had too much freedom. You grew up wilful and indifferent to the needs and wishes of others.'

'Your needs, your wishes, you mean!' she exclaimed accusingly.

'I was your husband!' he retorted.

'Keeper,' she threw back at him. 'You were my keeper, you owned me, the way you might have kept a stray kitten you'd picked up in the street. Oh, I had my silk cushion and plenty of cream, but I had no share in your real life, Andreas. Your family mattered more than I ever did. I was just a plaything.'

She moved to get up and his hand retrieved her casually, yet with a power she could not fight, pulling her back towards him so that her body lay against him. 'A plaything with claws,' he said with a thickness in his voice. 'You marked me more than once, Lauren.'

'Only when you played too roughly with me,' she retorted, her lashes down over her eyes.

'You didn't entirely dislike rough handling, did you?' he asked mockingly, one finger tracing the stubborn line of her mouth, leaving a heat wherever it touched.

'I hate you,' she whispered.

He leaned closer. 'That might make it a challenge, Lauren, hadn't that occurred to you? I might find that hatred of yours a stimulant more than a deterrent.'

Heart beating faster, she said bitterly, 'Only to a brute who enjoyed hurting women.'

That annoyed him; she heard his intake of breath. His hands bit into her, shaking her. 'Don't make me angry,' he warned, 'or you'll find out just how much of a brute I can be.'

'I don't need a second lesson,' she said, flicking a cold look at him. 'I already know.'

Andreas was silent for a moment, she felt his eyes observing her but did not look up again. Then he murmured, 'Is Colby a brute, Lauren?'

She felt her cheeks stain with hot colour. 'Philip?'

'Is he?' Andreas insisted. 'I always thought him a lapdog rather than a man. Don't tell me you find him an adequate lover, my sweet?' And there was mockery in the endearment as he whispered it.

'I love Philip,' she said irritably. 'I'm not going to discuss him with you.'

'Do you use your claws on him or is it all sweetness and light between you?'

'Oh, shut up!' she broke out angrily, knowing he was deliberately tormenting her. 'Philip is patient and generous....'

'Patient? Oh, yes, he's that.' There was a strange, burning anger in Andreas' voice now. 'And always there, waiting for you, wasn't he? Even during our marriage you were always stealing off to him.'

'I was painting in my father's studio! Philip just happened to visit us now and then.'

He laughed harshly. 'Your painting ... such a convenient excuse!'

That hit her hard and her eyes opened wide with

anger, glaring at him. 'Believe it or not, I'm a damned good painter, so you can keep your sneers to yourself. I'm beginning to make a name, damn you.'

'Colby is making a name for you, you mean,' he slipped in smoothly. 'You once told me yourself that a dealer would make or break an artist, and Colby has made very sure he pushed your work whenever he got the chance. You're his creation as far as art goes.'

'That's a lie,' she retorted, clenching with anger. 'You just hate to admit a woman can be good at anything.'

'On the contrary,' he drawled with a long, insolent stare, 'women are very good for one thing.'

Lauren's face flamed as she absorbed the remark. 'You should know,' she bit back. 'You've had enough of them!'

'Not enough,' he said, his hand turning up her face before she could escape. 'Oh, no, Lauren.'

She pulled her head back, but his hand was on the back of her neck, forcing her forward, and when his mouth found hers there was a very different intention in the kiss. Andreas turned a slow, deliberate sensuality upon her, languorously exploring the contours of her mouth at leisure.

She would not respond. She held herself rigidly even though her senses were inflamed by the seductive movements of his lips.

He lifted his head and they stared at each other. 'Colby hasn't taught you much,' he said insultingly.

'He's taught me to find casual sex revolting,' she said bitingly, then she escaped while he was off guard and ran out of the room. She sought the wild freedom of the cliffs and shore, finding in the bracing rush of the wind, the cry of the seabirds, the comfort she needed.

It was her own fault. Jimmy and Philip had warned her. Her own common sense had warned her. Andreas had been playing out a charade and she had fallen for it like a fool, trapped by her own weakness for a man she ought to hate.

Jimmy had tried to force her to face the facts, but she had refused, although the facts had been blatant enough. She had come here willingly.

She covered her face with her hands. Oh, God, how willingly, she thought in humiliation. A lamb to the slaughter. Andreas had not pulled the wool over her eyes, she had done it herself, silently co-operating with him in his charade. Lydia had known that, had more or less said as much, and no doubt that was why Lydia had agreed to help Andreas by lying, because it had been so obvious that Lauren wanted to go along with the pretence.

'I ought to have had more pride,' she told herself contemptuously. Her eyes fell on the wide band of her wedding ring. Angrily she pulled it off, tempted for a moment to fling it into the sea. But she couldn't do it. With a grimace she pushed it into her pocket. At least now she need not keep up the pretence, she thought. It was doubly infuriating that Andreas might have seen through her own apparent belief in his charade, and guessed that she was eager to play along with him.

She walked on along the cliffs, struggling with herself. What was she going to do? The only way to get off the island was to go by boat and none of the fishermen would take her, however much she offered them. Andreas could make life hell for anyone who offended him. Even if she did manage to persuade someone to take her by boat there was the strong possibility that Andreas would pursue them and force her to come back. This was not England. Andreas was a powerful man with many interests in Greece. She would be helpless against his exercise of his power.

The wind was getting stronger, colder, biting through her suede jacket. She was tired, she suddenly realised, coming alive to the ache in her bones as she struggled against the wind. She had walked further than she realised. The villa was out of sight and it was going to take her a long time to walk back.

She shrugged. She would welcome physical exhaustion, it was easier to cope with than the confused state of her emotions. At least she might find it possible to sleep tonight.

Remembering that a narrow path led inland towards the villa she turned back from the cliff path and walked away from the sea, hoping to cut into the rough track eventually, making her way through the rough scrub and rocks, the ground uneven under her feet. There were few cars on the island. The people either walked or used the rough-coated little donkeys which could climb like goats on the steep hills. There were few inhabitants, anyway. A few farmers, a few fishermen, leading stark, hard-working lives here among the rocks and hills. The only way to leave the island, apart from flying, was to go by fishing boat, and that was out.

Andreas had thought it all out—she saw that now. It had never entered her head that she might be marooned with him here. She should have known. Perhaps she had, perhaps her subconscious had refused to let her think about that aspect.

The sound of an engine startled her so much that for a moment she was frozen in surprise, then she ran through the low windblown bushes, waving, staring towards the rough track and seeing the travelling blur of dust which had to be a car.

It was coming fast and she instinctively increased her speed, afraid the occupant wouldn't see her. She was so intent on the car that she did not see the rough outcrop of rock until too late. Her whole body jerked as she tripped over it. She fell hard, crying out, shocked by pain into a dazed silence as she lay full length among the wiry bushes, feeling nothing but the jarred ache of her bones.

Someone lifted her, turned her face upwards. Hands deftly, quickly, ran over her body, searching for possible injury. Lauren opened her eyes, wincing, and looked into a tanned thin face, saw dust-whitened fair hair and an anxious pair of bright blue eyes.

'You all right?' He had knelt beside her, still supporting her head with one hand after he had checked it for blood or bruising, and he spoke in English.

'Yes.' She didn't sound too sure, her voice faint, then because her inhibitions had been dissolved by the shock she said incredulously, 'You're English!'

He grinned at that, nodding. 'And so are you,' he said. 'How's that for a coincidence?'

'What are you *doing* here?'

'Snap,' he retorted.

She suddenly became aware that one of his hands

was resting on her waist in an intimate gesture which made her white face grow faintly pink. She sat up and the world went round in circles.

'Hey,' he said, his voice distinctly concerned. 'You shouldn't move. You took quite a knock.'

Lauren put her head down on her knees, her hands around her legs, taking slow deep breaths.

He left her like that for a moment and when the world had stopped spinning she slowly lifted her head.

'Better?' he asked, smiling at her.

She nodded. 'Thank you,' she added politely.

'I thought I was seeing things when you came running towards me,' he said.

'That makes two of us, because the last thing I expected to see was a car.'

'That figures,' he grinned. 'Few and far between on this island, aren't they? The only other one belongs to Keralides.' His blue eyes looked at her questioningly. 'But you must know that. Where else could you be staying? I heard he was back. You must be his nurse.'

She stared, taken aback, and answered before she had thought. 'His nurse? No.'

The blue eyes opened wide. 'No? But you're staying at the villa?' Then a new expression came into his face. 'Oh, sorry. I didn't mean to ask leading questions.'

Lauren could see what was in his mind. He didn't have to draw diagrams and the quick look he gave her left hand made it clear that he was mentally assessing her status and deciding that Andreas had brought one of his women with him, as, no doubt, he would have done if she had not been available, and jealousy made that a sickening conclusion. She looked angry and the man drew back, catching the flash of her green eyes.

Lauren got up and he moved to help her as she swayed slightly, still dizzy from her fall.

'I'll give you a lift back to your villa,' he said. 'That was what you wanted?'

'Thank you, yes,' she said, turning towards the functional vehicle standing on the track. He walked beside her, his blue eyes sliding down over her with interest and unconcealed masculine appreciation.

'We ought to introduce ourselves. I'm John Farrant.'

'Lauren Grey,' she told him.

'Lauren? That's unusual. But it suits you.'

He moved ahead and opened the door of the Land Rover. She climbed into it and he joined her, thrusting his long thin legs in their dusty beige slacks into position with casual force, switching on the ignition in the same movement. The engine throbbed and he set the Land Rover into motion.

'What are you doing on the island?' she asked him.

'I'm a sociologist,' he said, glancing at her.

She was astonished. 'Good heavens!'

A wry grimace touched his face. 'Why do people always respond like that, I wonder? What's so strange about the study of mankind?'

'Is that what you're doing here? Studying the islanders?'

'I'm making a tour of Greek islands observing the patterns of their society,' he said. 'Post-graduate stuff. I'm doing a thesis on isolated communities.'

'It sounds fascinating.'

'It is,' he said, and his voice was eager, a thread of excitement running through it.

'Where are you staying?' She thought of the few scattered little houses on the island and wondered which one was offering him shelter. What on earth did the people make of him, of what he was doing? How had he explained to them?

'At the villa,' he said, startling her into staring at him.

'What? But I haven't seen you there.'

'Ah, that's because I've been away,' he grinned. 'I went up into the mountains to visit Spiro's son Dimitri. I stayed there for a few days to note his working pattern and talk to him. Nice chap. We got on well.'

Helen had not mentioned any of this, Lauren thought. 'Does Andreas know you're at the villa?' she demanded, and John Farrant gave her a quick, intelligent look.

'I made the arrangement with him months ago. This is his Land Rover, in fact. He said I could use it to get around. You don't think I'd just walk into his house and treat it like a hotel without his permission or knowledge?'

'I'm sorry,' she apologised. 'Of course not. It's just that nobody had mentioned you. I had no idea there was a stranger on the island. How long are you staying?'

'Two more days,' he said casually, and it was then that the idea came to her. She drew in her breath sharply as it flashed into her mind and John Farrant looked round questioningly.

'How are you leaving?' she asked.

He grimaced. 'Boat. What else? I'm going on to my next stopping place. I drew up my itinerary a year ago.

I had a lot of advance arrangements to make, of course.'

Very casually she asked him: 'One of the fishermen taking you?'

He shook his head. 'A friend, actually. He's working on Crete and he has this boat. He's crazy about sailing. He's picking me up and dropping me at my next port of call, then going on alone for a few days to cruise around before he picks me up again.'

'English?' she asked, because that was important. If he was Greek he would hesitate to offend Andreas Keralides.

'More or less,' John Farrant said, and he laughed.

'What does that mean?'

'I think he has an English passport, but he hasn't lived there for years. He's a drifter. I met him in Turkey five years ago and since then he's been in Africa, Saudi Arabia and Greece. He works for a while until he's bored, then he skips off on his boat. As I said, he's boat crazy. It's what he lives for.'

Lauren breathed softly. 'Would he take a passenger?'

John Farrant turned and eyed her, brows rising into his floppy fair hair. 'You?'

'Me,' she nodded, watching as the villa swam into view, the long roof gleaming in wintry sunlight. 'I want to get off the island.'

'Does Keralides know?'

She said quickly, 'Don't tell him, please. He mustn't know. But I have to get away.' And her desperation was in her voice, making the point clear.

He whistled under his breath. 'Oh, I get it. I've heard he's something of a wolf.' He frowned. 'Why on earth did you come here with him if you feel like that?'

'I must have been out of my mind,' she said, her tone carrying conviction. 'Will you help me?'

He didn't even hesitate. 'Of course. You'll have to travel light, though. It isn't a big boat. All we could take is a small case and yourself, and you know you'll have to give a hand. Can you cook? That would be very handy.'

'I can cook,' she said, lightheaded with relief. 'Thank you—you can't imagine how grateful I am.'

He grinned at her. 'That will teach you to walk into hairy places, won't it? Your mother should have told you about men like Keralides.'

'I haven't got a mother,' she said, shivering, because it was true, someone should have warned her years ago before she ever met Andreas.

John Farrant's eyes softened. He gave her a kind look. 'Sorry. Forget I spoke.'

Lauren liked him. He was a nice man. She sensed that she could trust him. His eyes were straight and direct and, although he was aware of her as a woman, he was not aggressive about it, he merely noted it and let it go. She wouldn't have any trouble with him; she knew it.

They had reached the villa and he pulled up outside the main door. She climbed out stiffly, brushing dust from her clothes. The door swung open and Helen gazed at them impassively, dark eyes completely without expression. John Farrant grinned at her, slightly cheeky, friendly. 'Back again like a bad penny,' he said. 'Dimitri sends his love and I've got four kisses for you from your grandchildren.'

Helen gave him the slightest smile at that, unbending just a fraction, then her dark eyes moved back to Lauren. 'Where have you been? We have been worried about you. You have been gone for hours.'

'I took a long walk,' Lauren answered, moving to the door with John Farrant at her side.

'It is dangerous to walk too far from the villa, Mrs Keralides,' said Helen, and she was using the name deliberately. Lauren felt John Farrant stiffen, heard his intake of breath, and anger swept over her in a blinding rush.

'I am not Mrs Keralides,' she said icily, staring at Helen in cold challenge.

'You'll give Mr Farrant the wrong ideas, Lauren,' said a cool, mocking voice from behind Helen, and her heart skipped a beat as she saw Andreas standing there. 'Dispute it or not, my love, I have our wedding photos to prove it.' His mouth indented harshly. 'Little else, I admit, but give it time.'

John Farrant was scarlet and his eyes were angry. Lauren looked at him in despair and knew precisely what he was thinking. He imagined she had lied to him, deceived him, and he was furious with her. Shoving a hand around the back of his neck, he said brusquely, 'Excuse me, I need a shower and a change.'

He walked up the stairs and Lauren looked at Andreas bitterly. Helen vanished discreetly, leaving them alone in the hall. 'My God, I hate you!' she flung at him.

'Do you really?' Andreas sneered, and his face was savage. 'Well, I've got news for you, my darling. What you feel for me is lukewarm compared to what I feel for you.'

CHAPTER SIX

THE remark took her by surprise. She stared at him, her mouth open, and he gave a cold malicious smile.

'That took the wind out of your sails, did it?'

'*You* hate me?' She was conscious of a peculiar mixture of reactions to that, hurt and anger and burning resentment. 'It wasn't me who....'

'Wasn't it?' He lifted those heavy black brows in challenging sarcasm. 'Only a matter of time, though, wasn't it, before you gave Colby what you knew damned well he wanted.' He moved closer and she was no longer conscious of where they were, of possible eavesdroppers. His voice dropped to a harsh murmur. 'When, Lauren? Was it that night? Did you run from my house to his arms?'

Her heart was beating fiercely, painfully and she was beginning to shake. His closeness was overwhelming. While he lay ill in bed he had been somehow diminished, the powerful muscled strength of his lean body less obvious, but now he was on his feet again and although he still looked very pale he was intolerably male, his broad shoulders held stiffly under the crisp white shirt. The tight black curls were no longer able to give a touch of appealing youth to his hard face: his physical and mental arrogance saw to that. The arrogance in his cold eyes slashed through her pretence of indifference and made her wince away from him, backing like a frightened child.

'You've no right to ask me questions and I'm not answering them,' she flung uneasily back at him. 'Why did you lie to Mr Farrant? I'm not your wife any more. I'll tell him about the divorce. Do you think I won't?'

Andreas smiled grimly. 'I know you won't,' he said, taking her arm in one hand, his fingers pressing down into her flesh.

'I certainly shall!' She tried to pull her arm out of his grip, but he dug his fingers down, holding her remorselessly.

'You won't,' he said, 'because you won't be seeing him again. I'll kick him off the island. He can go to-night.'

'You can't do that!' But he could and they both knew it. All he had to do was order one of the fishermen to take John Farrant elsewhere and it would be done without question, and there was nothing John Farrant could do about it, because Andreas was master here and his will was all-powerful. Lauren threw back her blonde head, her green eyes defiantly angry.

'Can't I?' He sounded as though he would enjoy doing exactly as he had threatened. 'I can go further. I only have to whisper a word in the right places and his precious thesis goes whistling down the wind, because if I want him out of Greece, he'll be out, make no mistake about that. He'll suddenly find himself persona non grata everywhere he goes. Nobody will talk to him. Nobody will have him in their homes. He'll be on the next plane to England before he knows what's going on.'

'You swine!' she muttered, hating him, her voice shaking with it.

He tightened his hand cruelly, preventing her from backing away, staring into her angry face with narrowed, contemptuous eyes. 'I could be nastier than that,' he said. 'Just remember *that* when you get your next clever little idea for getting away, Lauren.'

She flushed. 'I don't know what you're talking about.'

'Oh, yes, you do. I'm not stupid. The moment you met Farrant you saw him as an escape route.'

'You can't stop him taking me with him.' She was whistling in the dark, though, because she knew he could.

He laughed unpleasantly. 'Try it. Just try it. I'd have you off the boat in two seconds flat.'

'You can't keep me here against my will!'

'Your will?' He smiled then, a cruel mockery in his dark eyes. His free hand came up and fingered her throat, pressing into the soft warmth of her skin, starting violent pulses beneath the movements of the long fingers. 'We'll see how strong your will-power is, shall we, Lauren?'

'No,' she stammered, and her breathing became fast and shallow as Andreas dragged her head forward, his fingers hurting on her neck.

He found her mouth, forcing her head back, savagery in the pressure of his lips on hers. Lauren twisted and pushed, but she was helpless against his strength and then it was all too late anyway, because something had happened inside herself, some five-year-old blockage had abruptly melted away and long-denied emotions were erupting within her. Andreas felt the melting of her body and his kiss altered in response. Lauren's arms went round his neck, her hands pushing into his dark hair, her whole body tilted to arch against him, and she was groaning, her lips parting in a fevered response. 'Oh, God,' Andreas muttered thickly, moving his hands down her back, stroking, caressing.

A footstep split them apart. They sprang back, flushed, breathing heavily, their eyes bewildered, because in those few moments everything else had faded out of existence and only the burning urgency of their own needs had mattered.

John Farrant gave them a quick, embarrassed look. 'Oh, sorry,' he mumbled. 'I didn't know. . . .'

Andreas regained control first. 'Ah, Mr Farrant,' he said, smiling coolly, sauntering forward. 'Come and have a drink. You must want your lunch. Helen should have it ready soon.'

'Thank you.' John Farrant glanced awkwardly at Lauren, who looked away, guessing that he must be thinking her a liar. From his point of view it must look as though she had involved him in some marital squabble with his host, embarrassing and putting him on the spot.

'I must change,' she said huskily, turning towards the stairs.

'Do that, darling,' said Andreas, and he was laughing at her, she heard the amusement in his deep voice.

She ran up to her room and showered, changing into a cream silk dress with a low, scooped neckline and full, pleated sleeves which rippled softly against her arms as she moved. It clung tightly to her slender body, emphasising every curve from breast to thigh. She clipped around her throat a necklace Philip had given her, six rows of fine gold chains which glittered as she turned her head from side to side, observing them thoughtfully. Andreas had given her some very lovely, very expensive jewellery, but she had left it all behind when she fled.

She eyed herself in the mirror, critically, seeing with impatience her over-heated skin and fever-bright eyes. What had come over her, responding to Andreas like that?

There was a deep-seated aching in the centre of her body, an aroused hunger which she recognised with reluctant dismay. She had wanted to be immune to him, but in so short a time his lovemaking had brought it all back; the drowning sensuality which had always engulfed her when he had her in his arms.

What exactly was Andreas trying to do to her? Why had he brought her here, tricked and trapped her, made her a prisoner?

Her pulses beat fiercely as she considered his motives, knowing, against her will, that she already guessed at one of them, because when he was kissing her she had not been the only one to become so fiercely aroused. She had discovered that as her body swayed against his, feeling him pulse with an urgency she remembered only too well.

She had to make herself remember other things, remind herself that Andreas reacted to all attractive women with the same force. It was a purely physical reaction in him and she was not going to let him use her for some brief satisfaction of his masculine appetite.

Although it had been his own infidelity which had destroyed their marriage it was already clear to her that Andreas felt he was the one with the grievance. His whole attitude indicated that he felt she was the one to blame. Lydia had as good as told her so, had seemed to share Andreas's view, obscurely appearing to offer pity only to him. Lifting her blonde head angrily, Lauren spun and went downstairs, meeting Andreas's speculative stare with a cold hauteur which merely made him smile.

He placed a glass of sherry in her hand and turned to John Farrant courteously. 'My wife is an artist, you know, quite a talented one.'

John Farrant's eyes skimmed over her, were quickly withdrawn. 'Oh, really? Professionally or ... ?'

The question annoyed Lauren. 'I'm very professional, Mr Farrant,' she snapped, a coin of red in each cheek.

'Lauren likes to be taken seriously, don't you, *eros mou*?' Andreas murmured the words teasingly, mockingly, and there was a good deal more below the surface than he allowed to appear.

She turned and gave him a freezing look. 'Yes,' she said, daring him to smile, 'I do.'

'I'm sure you're very good,' John Farrant said clumsily, trying to appease, to lessen the tension which he could feel between them. 'Did you train? I mean, did you go to art college?'

'Yes,' she said, giving him a crisp rundown on her training, her green eyes impatient as she surveyed him.

'Good lord!' he exclaimed suddenly, staring. 'Are

you. . . .' His colour swam up suddenly and he glanced at Andreas. 'You did say your name was Grey once. Any relation to Jimmy Grey, the artist?'

'My father,' Lauren told him, conscious of Andreas's eyes and knowing that he had guessed she had given John Farrant her maiden name when she introduced herself.

'He's very good,' the young man said, then laughed. 'But you know that. I don't need to tell you.'

'Yes, my father is a very good painter,' she agreed. 'I'm proud of him.'

'My wife is better,' Andreas said coolly, surprising her so much that she stared at him in disbelief. He didn't look at her, his eyes on John Farrant's thin face. 'Come and see,' he added, walking gracefully towards the door, his lean body moving slowly but with something of his old power.

Puzzled, incredulous, she followed them after a pause and Andreas opened the door of a room she had not been inside since her arrival, a little sitting-room which Lydia used almost exclusively on her visits, the white walls and deep blue carpet giving it a Mediterranean simplicity which was now emphasised by the canvases hanging round the walls.

Lauren couldn't move. She just stood there, staring, her face white, her eyes enormous.

One after the other she recognised the pictures. They had been painted over the last three years and she had never guessed that Andreas had acquired them. Had Philip even suspected? Or had he preferred not to tell her?

Andreas watched as John Farrant slowly walked

round the room studying them. Lauren stared at her husband's hard, dark profile. Why? Why had he bought them? Why hang them here all together like this?

They were mainly landscapes, some painted in the South of France and capturing the vivid blue of the sky, the brilliance of sun and water; some painted in the stormy grey skies of northern England when she was staying in an isolated village in the heather-clad hills of a remote county. There was strange contrast between the two backgrounds, but the same mind lay behind both and it showed, both in use of colour and choice of perspective and in technique. The brush strokes grew stronger, more certain, as she learnt what she was doing, but even in the beginning she recognised now that she had had a certain gift, a visual appeal.

Andreas turned his black head and his eyes searched her face. 'Interesting to see them all together like this, isn't it?' He might have been speaking to John Farrant, but in fact he was talking to her, his expression told her so.

John Farrant turned then and smiled at her, admiration in his face. 'Your husband's right—you are good. If you're proud of your father, I'll bet he's proud of you.'

'Thank you,' she said, flushing, but she was still chiefly involved in puzzling over Andreas's motive for buying her pictures. Suddenly she stiffened. Had he been playing patron? Trying to help her make a start? Her success from the start in selling her paintings had been an enormous encouragement, had made her more confident, helped her to find her feet quickly. If it had

been Andreas's doing it changed her view of herself because she had prided herself on making her own way
unaided and how could she be sure she had done so if
Andreas had secretly been bolstering her confidence
like this?

Helen stood in the doorway. 'Lunch,' she said, adding in Greek that it would be spoiled if they did not
come at once and was Andreas mad getting up like
this? He would be sorry tomorrow. He wasn't strong
enough yet for all this entertaining.

'Shut up,' said Andreas, rudely, in English, but his
dark eyes smiled at Helen as he said it, accepting that
she was only worried about him and reassuring her.

'I think you should have your lunch in bed,' Lauren
said. 'I'm surprised the nurse allowed you to get up.'

'Allowed!' he echoed, eyes scornful. 'That woman
can't dictate to me whether I get up or stay in bed.'
Then his glance grew taunting as he added softly, 'The
only woman who gets me into bed at a word is you,
eros mou.'

Her cheeks burned, she was furious with him, conscious of two pairs of listening ears, aware that Helen
was now smiling broadly, that John Farrant was looking pink around the neck.

'Then I'll say the word now,' she retorted, using his
own teasing against him. 'Go to bed, Andreas. You
should never have got up.'

'Alone?' he asked, flickering a dark eyebrow towards
her, that tormenting smile in his eyes, observing with
open satisfaction the dark flush rising in her face.

She turned away, trembling, furious, and walked
towards the door without saying another word, unable

to speak because she would have said something which would have precipitated a violent explosion in front of Helen and John Farrant. How dared he? His uncaring insolence was breathtaking. She screwed her hands into small balls beside her hips, biting her lip, gnawing the smooth inner skin until it bled. How dared he?

He had betrayed her with Martine, hurt her beyond bearing, and yet now he stood there, dark, insolent and assured, mocking her as though the past had never existed. Her eyes were hot with the pressure of unshed tears. She had to breathe deeply to control her own trembling body, somehow force down the savage emotions sweeping over her.

The lunch was a difficult occasion. Lauren felt sorry for John Farrant, whose nervous eyes betrayed his awareness of the electric tension between his companions, his stammered comments lapsing now and then into heavy silence.

Feeling impelled to make conversation, she deliberately led him into talking about his work, knowing that shop talk was always the easiest form of conversation for people who liked their job. He eagerly plunged into explanation, discussion, speaking with more freedom once he was on his hobbyhorse, and somehow the hour passed without another brittle incident between herself and Andreas.

Indeed, Andreas looked rather white, she thought anxiously, as they rose after the meal, and she said to him irritably, 'You really must get some rest, Andreas. You look ill.'

He must have felt weak because he shrugged rather bleakly and excused himself to John Farrant with a brief smile before moving to the stairs. 'Come with me, Lauren,' he said sharply, looking at her. 'I'd like your arm on these stairs. They are a bit much for me.'

He leant on her shoulder on the stairs, his breathing jerky, and she eyed him with concern. There were dark shadows under his eyes now, revealing great weariness.

'Why on earth did you get up?' she burst out as he collapsed on to his bed with the nurse clucking around him, with an expression of distinct 'I told you so.'

He lay back, one hand loosening his collar, his heavy lids half closed, staring at her with a slight, mocking smile. 'You wouldn't come to me, so I came looking for you.'

She felt her face colour and looked away. 'Well, now you must stay in bed for the rest of the day.'

'Indeed you must,' the nurse commented. 'If you refuse to take my advice, Mr Keralides, there's no point in my staying. You've been very ill, remember. Rest is essential.'

Andreas grimaced, his lips white. 'Don't fuss, woman,' he said, his tone deep but weary.

Lauren walked to the door, leaving her to get him into bed, and he stared after her. 'Where are you going?'

She halted at the door. 'I think I'll take a siesta myself,' she said. 'That walk this morning was very tiring.'

'Very sensible,' said the nurse, nodding at her.

Andreas jeered teasingly, 'Getting soft, Lauren? One little walk and you're exhausted?'

'That's right,' she said, slipping out of the room, and heard him laugh as she shut the door.

In fact she was even more tired than she had realised,

because the moment she lay down on her bed, the blinds down to plunge the room into comfortable shadow, she fell fast asleep.

When she woke the room was totally black with that endless lightlessness which only the countryside can confer on the sky when there are no artificial, manmade lights to break up the pall of darkness. Sleepily, aware of hot face and untidy rumpled hair, she got up and switched on her bedside lamp, illuminating her room with a softness which made her blink as though dazzled.

Glancing at her watch, she realised with a shock that she had slept for five hours. It was long past the dinner hour at the villa and she wondered if Helen had looked in and seen her deeply asleep.

There was a pang of hunger at the thought that she had missed the meal, making her aware that she needed food now that she was awake. She rapidly brushed her hair, leaving it on impulse hanging loose around her flushed face, splashed her skin with cool water and dried it carefully, applying the lightest make-up afterwards, the warm glow of her skin needing little aid to make it bloom into life, her lips touched with light pink.

She halted outside Andreas's door to listen. Was he still asleep, or had he eaten dinner at the usual hour? There was silence in the room, giving her no clues, but as she moved away on tiptoe the door suddenly opened behind her and she turned quickly to find Andreas standing there in a black silk dressing-gown and silk pyjamas.

'Awake at last?' he asked teasingly. 'I thought you

were never going to wake.'

'I was tired.'

'You looked like a little girl, curled up on your side,' he said, and her heart at once began to beat thunderously as she realised that he had been into her room while she slept, had stood there watching her at her most vulnerable, seeing her without the masks which custom and willpower made possible.

It unnerved her and she retreated into anger, flaring up, her eyes brilliantly green. 'Keep out of my room, Andreas!'

His warmly teasing expression vanished and the dark eyes took on a cold, implacable look. He grabbed her arm and pulled her towards his room. 'Let me go!' she bit out, struggling.

'Helen left you some supper,' he said, ignoring her.

'I'll eat downstairs.'

'You'll eat where I tell you.'

'Damn you,' she snapped, 'stop pushing me around!'

He closed the door with his foot and let her go, leaning against the door, his broad shoulders resting on the panels. 'Sit down and eat your supper,' he said coldly.

Helen had left a tray covered with a white damask cloth. Reluctantly Lauren took off the cloth and her stomach at once warned her that she was very hungry. The smell of the food was irresistible, even though it was cold. Helen had always made good sandwiches. These were tiny little triangles of springy Greek bread, their texture creamy and with that characteristic nutty scent, the fillings a selection of meats and salad vege-

tables. Grimacing at her own weakness, she sat down
and began to eat. Andreas turned on the hotplate set
into an alcove of his bedroom and within a few
moments the odour of coffee filled the room. He
poured them both a cup, rich, thick dark Greek coffee
heavily steeped in sugar and quite milkless.

'That's too strong for you,' she told him, and he
gave her a frowning look in reply.

'I'm old enough to decide what's bad for me and
what isn't,' he retorted. His coffee had no sugar in it,
she noticed, and was as black as night and as thick as
mud. He had always been a coffee addict, drinking cup
after cup of the stuff, always this strong, but then he
had just been through the results of a very serious
accident.

'It must be bad for your nerves!' she told him.

'It's bad for my nerves to be frustrated,' he said
softly, sending a wave of angry colour into her face.

'I'm not listening to remarks like that,' she burst out
angrily. 'How can you talk to me like that? After what
you did!'

'What did I do?' he asked with a sudden harsh note
in his voice.

Lauren looked at him almost dazedly, taken aback.
'You know very well what I mean!'

'Tell me,' he clipped out, his face all angles.

She could have thrown the boiling coffee into his
face, her hands shaking with the desire to hit him.
'Don't pretend your memory has gone again,' she
taunted.

'My memory is perfect,' Andreas told her grimly.
'How's yours?'

'Oh, every detail comes back as sharp as a knife,' she said, her voice feverish, the green eyes wide and bitter in her hot face. 'I saw you, remember. Do you think I've forgotten one iota of what I saw?'

Andreas thrust his hands deep into the pockets of his dressing-gown, staring at her. 'No,' he said heavily, 'I don't suppose you have.'

The admission hurt her with a ferocity which was like a sword plunging into her heart. They had never spoken of it before. She hadn't seen him from the moment she walked into her bedroom and saw Martine in his arms. Now she looked at him with trembling anguish, hatred in her eyes.

'How can you treat it so lightly? Did you expect me to ignore what you'd done? Would you? If you had been the one to walk in and see me in someone else's arms would you just have said, "Oh, sorry, excuse me," and walked cheerfully out again?'

The savage flame of his eyes spoke for him before he said, 'Because I didn't see you with Colby, does that make it any easier for me, do you think?'

'I've never....' She broke off there, furious with herself, because she had deliberately given him the impression that she had slept with Philip and it was a small sop to her pride, a tiny ray of comfort, for him to believe that.

He hadn't missed the implication of her denial, his eyes were sharp and narrow, searching her face. 'Haven't you? You said you had. All these years, seeing him all the time, and you expect me to believe you're not his lover?'

'My relationship with Philip is none of your busi-

ness,' she threw back. 'Anyway, I'm going to marry
him. You do remember that, I hope? We got engaged.'

His lip curled back in fury over his teeth. 'Oh, I remember it. It was all that was in my mind as I drove
that day.'

Lauren put a shaking hand over her mouth. 'When
you crashed?'

'When I crashed,' he agreed thickly, those little
flames in his dark eyes.

She pulled herself together. 'Now I suppose you're
trying to claim it was my fault you crashed?'

He shrugged that aside. 'It was my own fault for
being so stupidly affected by reading the announce-
ment in the papers that morning. If I'd had my mind
on what I was doing I would have seen the oil before
I hit it.'

'Too bad that for once your wonderful concentration
wasn't working properly,' she mocked coldly. 'I thought
nothing ever came between you and your work.'

She had gone too far, she knew that as she saw the
little flames burst into full-scale conflagration. She got
to her feet too late. Andreas had her, his hands violent,
and as his mouth closed with hers she knew she had
been waiting for it ever since she woke up. She was
a long way past pretending. She wanted to feel that
hard male body forcing her down on to the bed and she
didn't even begin to struggle when it did. They kissed
each other with hungry intensity, heat flaming between
them. He had taught her body the motions of passion
and now she realised how eagerly she wanted to experience them again with him, her hands sliding under the
heavy quilted black silk to touch his bare skin, a shud-

der of urgent desire running through her as she let her hands go where they pleased.

Andreas gave a stifled groan as he felt her hands moving over his body. His mouth explored hers deeply, brushing her bruised lips like a salve. His fingers pushed through her hair, fondling it, stroked her nape, moved to her hollowed throat, where a fast pulse beat, betraying to him her excitement. 'Tell me,' he whispered harshly against her lips. 'Tell me ... is Colby your lover? Has he been?'

The question shattered her mood like a blow. Memory flooded back and she hated herself for the mindless sensuality which had taken over her body, making her forget what Andreas had done, what he would just as easily do in the future.

'Let me go!' she gasped, struggling to free herself.

'Answer me,' he demanded, and she looked bitterly into his dark eyes.

'Yes,' she almost shouted. 'Yes!'

He hit her, the blow almost knocking her head off her neck. Ears ringing, she stared at him in shock.

'You swine!'

He hit her again and tears sprang into her eyes, she was shaking, suddenly terrified because there was savage jealousy in his eyes and he was a black stranger, a primitive barbaric enemy who might do anything.

She lay there watching him like a frightened animal, eyes very wide, while he breathed thickly, staring at her, as though even he wasn't sure what he meant to do next, as though he were fighting for control over emotions raging through his blood like a fatal disease.

'It was never my intention to see you again,' he said bleakly at last.

'I hoped to God I'd never see you,' Lauren muttered, bending her head, then lifting it because she had found herself looking at the bared throat which a moment before she had kissed and at once her treacherous senses had leaped with the desire to put her mouth to it again.

'Yes,' he groaned huskily. 'We've hurt each other too deeply for either of us to forget.'

That made her blood boil. 'We've hurt each other? What did I ever do to you?. You committed adultery, not me, Andreas.'

The black eyes were piercing as he stared at her face. 'You've just admitted that the night you walked out of my house you went to Colby.'

Wearily she shrugged. 'I went to my father. Philip wasn't even there.'

'But you did see him some time that night,' Andreas said tightly.

'No.'

'Don't lie to me,' he broke out, his face furious. 'I know you did, Lauren. You were in Colby's bed that night.'

She stared, eyes angry. 'No!'

Andreas swore viciously. 'You damned little liar! Colby himself admitted it.'

Lauren felt waves of shock break over her. 'What are you talking about? When did Philip say....'

'I came to your house next day.' Andreas pushed her away abruptly, swung off the bed and walked to the other side of the room, fingering a shelf of books as though suddenly fascinated by their spines. 'He told me then.'

Lauren went ice-cold, remembering the fight she had heard, Philip's high angry voice, the harsh tones of Andreas's demands. Philip had lied to him. Why? Or couldn't she guess, and be grateful, realising now that Philip had tried to salve her pride, to repay Andreas in his own coin, because by then Philip had heard from her how she had walked in and found Martine in bed with Andreas. She had been distraught when she sobbed out the story, the sight of the two of them had destroyed her, and Philip had been grim as he listened. So he had lied to Andreas for her. Her sigh made Andreas turn and stare at her.

'I should have cited Colby when we were divorced, but it would only have given the gossip columnists food.'

'There was enough excitement for them when you married Martine,' she said maliciously. 'Especially since she was on the point of giving birth to your child.'

His mouth twisted. Jerkily he walked back to her, staring down at her. 'Colby never told me when....' He broke off, his teeth biting into his lip. 'Did you go to him after you had seen me....'

She knew, of course, what he was asking, and she heard the note in his voice which he was fighting to suppress. 'I've no intention of discussing it,' she said, her lids down over her eyes.

His hands came down on her slender shoulders, drawing her up towards him, shaking her. 'Oh, for God's sake, it matters, can't you see I've got to know?'

She gave him a cool, contemptuous glance, her green

eyes sheathed by the white lids. 'Your vanity needs to believe I only went to Philip because you had already been unfaithful to me, does it?'

His hands bit into her, his eyes were molten with rage and emotion. 'You bitch!' he muttered.

He frightened her, but she scooped up her courage from deep within her nature and said icily, 'At least I don't have a child to prove it.'

Andreas flinched. She saw the tremor pass over his hard face, his eyes went quite black, as though his eyes were all pupil, the iris lightless. 'God,' he said hoarsely. 'Oh, God, I could kill you!'

'*You* could kill *me*?' She arched her brows in cool hauteur. 'You always did see everything from your own angle, Andreas, but I didn't imagine that even you could see your adultery in such a flattering light that you blamed me for it.' She pushed at his broad chest, pulling away. 'May I go now, please? This discussion is boring me.' She forced herself to speak politely, coldly, her face chilling.

He stared at her for a moment without speaking, breathing thickly, then he smiled, and that smile was a weapon in itself, it savaged her, sending a shiver of horror down her spine, leaving her shaken and suddenly very aware that she was in his bedroom alone with him and there was no one to whom she could scream for help.

'Oh, no, *eros mou*,' he said softly, very softly. 'I haven't finished with you yet.'

Her face went white. She abandoned pride because this now was a conflict too bitter for it to be any use to her. 'If you touch me I'll hate it,' she whispered in a thin, scared voice.

He laughed, and there was naked desire in his eyes, a feeling so powerful that she went rigid with terror in front of it. He had never before looked at her like that. No man had. Andreas had often looked at her with passion in the past, but always with love too, and now there was nothing warm or soft about the expression in those beautiful dark eyes. She had never seen that expression in a man's face before, but she knew it now, she had no hesitation in recognising it.

Lust, she thought sickeningly. It was an ugly word for an uglier feeling, but it was what she saw in his face as she stared at him. His eyes were as hard as obsidian, inhuman, glittering, and his nostrils flared white above his mouth.

'Don't,' she whispered. 'Please!'

His hands moved slowly and she watched them, stricken with fear, unable to move because her heart was thudding in her throat and she was paralysed.

'You've had five years to learn how to please a man,' he said thickly. 'I want to know how much Colby has taught you.'

She broke from the spell of her terror too late, struggling wildly in the remorseless hands, scratching, biting, kicking. 'I'd rather die,' she moaned.

'You can die afterwards,' Andreas retorted in harsh mockery, forcing her inexorably backwards on to the bed, pushing her arms back over her head so that she writhed helplessly, pinioned by his hard body, while he watched her as if enjoying her attempts to escape.

'Oh, God, I hate you!' she spat out, at last lying

still, facing the pointlessness of her struggle.

'Good,' he said. 'That makes it perfect.' Then he lowered his head and kissed her throat, moving his mouth slowly down the warm skin in an unhurried enjoyment which had her gasping. He freed one of her arms, took hold of her bodice and casually ripped it down to her waist. The silk tore with a thin sound and she said childishly,

'You've ruined my dress.'

Andreas laughed softly. 'I'll buy you another,' he whispered, kissing her white breasts slowly, his lips hot against them. 'But make it worth my while, *eros mou.*'

She did not want to experience the sensation which was running through her body. She fought against it, as she had fought against his hands a moment ago. His hands were on her bare skin, exploring her with the curiosity of revisited dreams, and she closed her eyes so that she could pretend that that was all that was happening to her, that she was dreaming as she had often dreamt before.

He was breathing thickly as he lifted his head. His mouth came down and destroyed her last refuge, stripping away her pretence that it was a dream, bringing her fiercely awake. She went down under the tidal wave of desire which was swallowing him too, and from that moment she gave up the unequal struggle.

She no longer cared, anyway, she admitted, because there was sweet feverish delight in everything he did to her. She moaned softly in his hands, trembling violently, knowing she rode a whirlwind which would destroy her but no longer giving a damn.

Later, she knew, she would despise and hate herself, but now she was past thinking of anything but the easing of a long-unsatisfied need to touch and be touched by him, all her control gone, her inhibitions dissolved, sunk in an abandonment which was like nothing she had ever known before as for the first time in five long empty years Andreas possessed her, body and soul.

CHAPTER SEVEN

SHE woke next morning feeling exhausted, her head throbbing, her face grey. For a few minutes after their fierce lovemaking she had lain beside Andreas, eyes closed, breathing heavily, then repulsion and self-disgust had swept over her and she had run from him as though from the devil himself. For hours she had paced her room, shaking, ice-cold, and she had only fallen asleep as the thick pall of darkness began to thin into dawn.

Glancing at the tiny gold clock beside the bed she saw that it was ten o'clock. Reluctantly she got up and showered, dressed in a fine white linen dress with a pleated cape collar, brushing her sleek blonde hair into a chignon which she pinned with trembling fingers.

Helen eyed her expressionlessly when she descended. 'Coffee and croissant?' she asked in her deep voice.

'Thank you.' Lauren stood by the window staring out at the grey sky, shivering. When Helen brought her breakfast she sat down and poured herself some coffee, drank it black, needing the heat and strength it gave her. She could not touch the food, after one look at it she pushed it away. Helen's mouth indented.

'Andreas ate nothing either,' she said, and Lauren's face flooded with colour, her lids trembled as she looked away.

'He is staying in bed today,' Helen said. 'He overdid it yesterday.'

Lauren laughed hysterically and couldn't stop. She knew Helen was staring at her with unhidden curiosity. Summoning up spirit from somewhere she forced herself to regain control, her sleek shining head bent over her coffee.

John Farrant walked in a moment later and gave her a polite nod. 'Good morning, Mrs Keralides.'

'Good morning,' she said, glancing at him and away. She still found it embarrassing to remember how she had talked him into taking her away only to have Andreas spike her guns later. No doubt the man thought her contemptible. Andreas was right in one thing, though : there was no point in enlightening John Farrant as to the complexities of their relationship.

'I'm leaving today, after all,' he said with a strange note in his voice, and she felt herself flush, guessing that Andreas had arranged his early departure.

'Well, it was nice to meet you,' she said, moving to the door. 'I hope you have a good trip.'

'The sea seems quite calm today,' he agreed, watching her.

'Is your friend coming for you or are you taking a fishing boat?'

'Your husband telephoned my friend,' he said, and there was distinct amusement in his blue eyes. She flushed, knowing that he imagined Andreas had been jealous, had wanted him off the island in case she ran off with him.

It didn't matter now, because she was certain Andreas would let her go after last night. It had been a Pyrrhic encounter for both of them, consuming them in a brief insanity which had left her burnt out, empty, and no doubt had done the same to Andreas.

'I hope your thesis goes well,' she said politely. 'Good luck with it.'

'Thank you,' John Farrant answered, smiling, and she walked out, leaving him staring after her.

She walked along the cliffs and watched the silver sea glint under wintry sunlight, the waves calm and flat as a millpond, while far away the line of the horizon was streaked with blue and wreathed with luminous mist here and there.

She heard the Land Rover engine as she walked back to the house and waved as John Farrant passed her. He was going to the quayside to meet his friend, no doubt, and there was a rucksack and large checked bag beside him.

'He's gone,' Helen said with satisfaction as Lauren ate her lunch alone. The smell of the aromatic herbs with which the lamb had been cooked made her feel sick again, but she forced herself to eat some of the tender meat. It fell off the bone as she touched it with her fork and she smiled at Helen.

'You're such a wonderful cook!'

Helen looked pleased, black eyes glinting. 'At least you are eating now.'

'Is Andreas?' Lauren wished she could recall the question as soon as it was out, but it had been asked and now Helen answered it, smiling.

'Yes, he is eating. He slept all morning. He was so tired, poor lamb.'

'I bet he was,' Lauren said viciously, then again

wished she could recall the remark, infuriated when Helen burst out laughing and went out, because what on earth had the woman believed she meant by her crack?

She spent the afternoon sketching a clump of grey rocks and some thistles, concentrating on them with intensity. She did not go anywhere near Andreas. She had not yet got the courage to face him. Perhaps he was staying in his own room because he was ashamed of what he had done—and somehow that thought made her angrier than ever.

It occurred to her that Andreas might have forced her submission to feed his own pride. She had divorced him, after all. Philip had told her of Andreas's rage the day he came to her father's house for her. Andreas had said 'She's mine,' and the possessive ring of that made her wince, because his whole background made it the remark of an owner, a possessor, and she could only permit such a sense of possession if love was the reason for it. But a lover does not betray, does not turn to other women. Andreas had a code which offended her to her very core. He had rules which applied to men but not to women. He had no shame in having slept with Martine, but he felt free to be jealously angry because he thought she had let Philip make love to her.

It twisted in her like a snake, the sense of self-betrayal which her uninhibited response to him had left. She felt it wash over her in icy floods whenever the memory flashed back.

Was it possible to hate and love at the same time? To despise and desire?

She closed her eyes, hearing the distant whisper of

the sea like mocking laughter. Oh, God, she thought, how I despise myself! It was so easy for him. I was only pretending to fight and he knew it. Five minutes and he could do what he liked with me. Have I no backbone at all?

Andreas came down to dinner. Lauren had not expected to see him and when he came into the room she felt pain lance her heart, leaving her white and trembling. She had been sitting on a brocade sofa, lazily turning the pages of a magazine. Looking up, she heard her own gasp of shock, felt her fingers shake on the pages.

He wore a white silk shirt and a formal dark suit, his hard lean figure dominating the quiet room. Closing the door, he leant against it and looked at her, his features giving nothing away, even the dark eyes unreadable.

She could not speak, only tilt her head proudly, defying him in silence.

He gave a twisted little smile. 'Nothing to say? That makes a change.'

She could speak then, the words unleashing temper in her as a sharp spur driven into flesh might do. 'What do you expect me to say? You know exactly how I feel. The very sight of you makes me sick!'

His eyes narrowed cruelly. 'That wasn't the impression I got last night.'

Her fingers curled into her palms, contempt in her green eyes. 'It may be news to you, but women can experience lust too. Even for men they loathe.'

The dark face tautened into a furious mask. 'I ought to throttle you for that!'

'Why, don't you like to hear the truth? What else

was it for either of us? You wanted me too, and in the same way.'

He withdrew, she could feel it, sense the sharp exclusion with which he straightened and clamped a mask down over his angry face. After a moment which seemed endless he said in a drawling voice, 'Oh, yes, *eros mou*, I wanted you.'

'Don't call me that!' Anguish had pierced through her as he said the words in that contemptuous tone.

'*Eros mou*,' he said again, tormenting her, knowing he was doing it, meaning to hurt.

She closed her eyes against the shaming possibility of tears. 'I hate you,' she whispered.

'How does it feel to burn with lust for someone you hate?' he asked, and his voice was nearer.

Lauren opened her eyes because she was instantly afraid and he was right beside her, his hands in his pockets, his tall dark figure looming over her, dwarfing her, making her aware of her weakness and vulnerability. The whole room was pulsing with electric tension. She leaned back against the back of the sofa, struggling to pull a calm look over her white face.

'It felt like hell,' she said through her taut lips. 'But now it's over.'

Andreas laughed in barbed mockery, teeth showing between his curled lips. 'Like hell,' he said. 'You think you can escape hell so easily? Say that again in a month's time and I might believe you.'

It shattered her composure. 'A month's time,' she repeated, her voice shaking. 'No, you can't. Andreas, for God's sake!'

'You think I'd let you go after last night?' He arched

one dark brow, taunting her, his eyes filled with a glittering angry amusement.

'Wasn't it enough?' She knew that despair had filled her voice and she could do nothing about it. 'You'll destroy me. Let me go!'

'Colby won't want you now,' he drawled, and there was hard satisfaction in his voice. 'Once or a hundred times, what difference would it make to him? The fact that you let me have it again would stick in his throat.'

Her face flamed with angry colour. 'Is that why?'

He bent, putting a finger under her chin, staring into her eyes. 'You know it wasn't.'

Yes, she knew, and she knew too that if she stayed here with him it would happen again because just the cool touch of his finger on her skin was driving her crazy and he knew it. He was smiling, watching her, eyes triumphant.

She pushed him away. 'You're despicable!' She got up and forced her way past him, turning at bay like a cornered animal, to glare defiance at him and know it was futile. 'Please—let me go. I can't stand this!'

Andreas gave a short laugh, his face hard. 'You came here of your own accord.'

'You trapped me.'

'My dear, the trap was obvious and you know it. You walked into it freely. I didn't make you come. How could I?'

'I believed you'd forgotten, that you were very ill.'

'Lie to yourself, but not to me,' he sneered. 'You came for the same reason I wanted you to come. It isn't over between us, Lauren. It never has been. It goes on eating at your insides, doesn't it? An unspeakable hunger you can't feed with anybody else.'

A wave of weakness swept her. She stared at him, her mouth dry, because he had described it exactly.

He read the response on her face and his lips twisted again. 'Yes,' he said softly.

Helen came then and Lauren heard her dimly announcing that the dinner was ready and were they coming or were they going to argue all night? Andreas answered in his quick, hard Greek, teasing Helen, retorting, not a whit abashed by the familiar teasing, apparently amused by it. Had Helen been listening, for God's sake? Lauren thought. Had she heard enough to know very well what was going on? That was a shaming thought. Her face burned with it as she followed Andreas to the table.

Only while they drank their coffee after the delicious meal did she consider the future. She had held it at bay through the meal but she could not evade it any longer. The food and wine had made her feel warmly at ease, but now the easiness vanished and she was tense, looking away from Andreas's dark features with her heart in her throat.

She pushed her coffee away and got up. He twisted, catching her wrist, his hand an iron bracelet forcing her to stand still.

'Where do you think you're going?'

'Bed,' she said shakily. 'I'm tired.'

The dark eyes surveyed her and she winced under them, all her colour gone, leaving her skin weary, waxen, her eyes full of dark shadows.

'Goodnight, then,' Andreas said in suddenly sombre tones, and his hand dropped, leaving her free.

She couldn't believe it, but she fled, shuddering. In her room she stood listening for sound of pursuit, but there was silence. She undressed and got to bed and lay there in the darkness with a tense sense of expectation, knowing that if he came he would get what he came for because she had neither will power nor energy to fight him tonight.

She never knew when she fell asleep. When she opened her eyes again, protesting at the invasion of the light, it was broad morning and the sunlight lay in glittering pools on the carpet.

The nurse was on the landing when she emerged from her room. She gave Lauren a faintly disapproving look. 'Are you coming to see your husband today, Mrs Keralides? He missed you yesterday.'

Lauren envied her the innocence which could see things without understanding them. Politely she said, 'Of course. When I've had my breakfast.'

'I shall keep him in bed again today,' the nurse said chattily. 'He keeps tiring himself. He should never have gone down to dinner last night.' Again there was reproof in her face. 'Perhaps you could visit him more often, then he wouldn't want to get up.'

Lauren wanted to laugh at that, but she made herself look cool and calm. She went down and Helen bustled out to greet her, eyeing her with those sardonic dark eyes. Over the coffee Helen suddenly said, 'You will only wear yourself out, fighting him. Andreas has never admitted defeat in his life.'

Lauren's cheeks bore spots of dark red. 'I'm not going to discuss my marriage with you, Helen.' She made herself sound polite but firm and was furious when Helen laughed.

'He was the same when he was small—pigheaded and possessive. Anything he owned was forbidden territory.'

'He doesn't own me!'

Helen looked unimpressed. 'No?'

Lauren got up, her chair thrust back violently. 'No, Helen. I own myself.'

But did she? she asked herself as she went up to see him. How could she claim to be in command of herself when Andreas could walk in and take her whenever he liked? She had no self-control where he was concerned. It angered her to admit it, even to herself, and it was humiliating that Andreas knew it as well as she did.

She walked into his bedroom stiffly, encased in dignity, and he looked up from the newspaper he was reading and saw the armour she was wearing with one brief, sardonic glance.

The nurse was tidying the medicines on a chest near the bed. She looked round, giving Lauren a comfortable, approving smile. 'You see, Mr Keralides, I told you she would come.'

Andreas looked imperturbable. 'So you did,' he murmured.

The nurse diplomatically withdrew with a final cosy smile at them and Lauren swung away to stare out of the window.

'While I'm here you can't see your son,' she said flatly. 'Don't you miss him?'

'Yes,' said Andreas. 'You met him at the hospital, Mama told me. What do you think of him?'

It hurt, but she said it. 'He looks like you.'

He laughed caustically. 'Is that a compliment or an insult to the poor boy?'

'Neither. It's a cold statement of fact,' she said.

He was silent and she turned to look at him. His features were enigmatic, the eyes guarded.

'Do you hate him because he's Martine's son?'

The question made her gasp in shock. After a moment she said hoarsely, 'I couldn't hate a child for any reason whatever.'

'But you prefer not to be reminded that he exists?' Andreas watched her remorselessly and she knew he was trying to pierce her features and discover the true state of her feelings towards his son.

'Would you want to see me with Philip's child?'

A raw, scraped fury flashed into his face, tightening his bones, hardening his eyes.

'No,' he said harshly.

Lauren was silent, looking at him. Was physical desire all he felt or was there another emotion beneath it? Could he be so bitter if there was nothing between them but lust?

'Niko is happy enough for the moment,' he said, almost as if he were talking to himself, reassuring himself.

She was only to be kept here for a month, she thought, while Andreas burnt out the fierce desire he felt for her, and then Niko could be reunited with his father and she would be forgotten. She stared at Andreas bitterly. It was degrading to be treated like this, she would never forgive him for it.

She walked to the door and Andreas asked sharply, 'Where are you going?'

'Anywhere but here,' she said sharply in retort. 'I find your company unbearable!'

She closed the door on whatever he had to say to that and escaped into the cold, clear air. She sketched for most of the day, forcing herself to concentrate on the work, filling her pad with fast, sharp impressions of what she saw. When she got back to England, her studio, she would have material enough to last a lifetime, but it would all be tainted by the bitterness of memory. She shuddered to think what dark chasms would be revealed if she painted anything she saw during this stay on the island. There was no barrier between hand and eye, no shutter she could run down to hide the emotions she was experiencing. She knew from past work that it all spilled out upon the canvas. The subconscious revealed feeling as though it were a voyeur retailing scandal. Even a landscape, the most innocent of subjects, could be translucent, self-exposing.

Andreas did not come down to dinner. She ate alone and Helen wore a reproachful air as she served her. Lauren ignored it, but it gnawed at her.

That night she could not sleep at all, she lay wide awake in her bed listening to the distant murmur of the sea and eaten alive with needs which left her white and exhausted in the morning. Andreas examined her face over breakfast thoughtfully and she knew he read the marks of her struggle with herself as though they were printed in black and white on her skin. She looked at him defiantly and he smiled, tormenting her, saying nothing, yet saying everything, because his mocking eyes told her he knew how badly she had wanted to admit defeat and crawl into his bed.

He came for a slow stroll around the garden with her later, pausing now and then to stare out over the sea. The air was çool and clear and the sky had a faint radiance as the sun lingered behind thin cloud.

Over dinner that evening his hand brushed hers as he passed her a roll. She felt her skin jerk at the contact and his eyes narrowed, that hard triumph in them.

She looked up, hating him, and he met her stare with cool knowledge, then his eyes drifted down to stare at her mouth and she could not control the trembling of her lips under his gaze.

'It gets harder,' he murmured very softly. 'It always does.'

'What are you talking about?' Lauren made herself sound sharp and slightly scornful, but he was not deceived.

'Addiction,' he said. 'However hard you fight, if it's in your bloodstream you need it, and the longer you struggle against it the worse the craving gets.'

'I won't let it happen again,' she said hoarsely, fleeing from him to her own room.

It was midnight when she gave in. The house had been absolutely silent for hours, but she knew Andreas was awake. He was not making a sound but the tentacles of his feeling were reaching out to her from his room and keeping her wakeful, brooding, fighting against herself as well as him.

When she opened the door the lamplight made a yellow circle in which he lay, watchful, his black head against his pillow, his eyes narrowing on her as she came into the room.

Slowly the black head lifted, the dark eyes moved over her, appraising the coffee-coloured silk nightgown, the matching negligee with its deep lace border.

He moved his hand and the lamp went out. Lauren came to him in the dark and his mouth hurt in that first, deep kiss, as though he were punishing her for the long struggle. The burning need had not been sated, she admitted at last. It seemed to have intensified. She knew she cried 'I love you, I love you,' and she no longer cared that it was a humiliating admission. She had lost all pride, yielding herself as though pierced with pleasure in the mere fact of being possessed by him, and Andreas took her savagely, using his strength, enforcing his dominance of her body without compunction. It was afterwards, when she cried helplessly, that he held her in his arms and kissed her face, her hair, her neck, offering her tenderness and gentleness, but only after he had made her submit without reserve.

She went back to her room in the pale light of dawn, leaving him sleeping, aware of a deep reluctance to leave his bed, to move away from the warmth of his body. She had slept only after tears which seemed to rend her mind and heart, but Andreas had held her, murmuring low and incoherent words of comfort, and she had been released into sleep still in his arms, her long hair silver in the darkness, entwined with his, straying over his naked shoulders, brushing his mouth. When she woke she lay still for a moment, hearing the deep beat of his heart under her cheek, feeling his limbs touch her own, his strong hand over her breast in a gesture of possession. It had been agony to go.

She was surprised when he came down to breakfast. Helen looked at him and her smile was warmly delighted. 'That is how you should look,' she nodded. 'Now I see my own Andreas again.'

One look told Lauren precisely what she meant. The grey tinge had gone from his skin. His eyes were alive, bright with health; his body moved with the old grace and catlike agility, his whole mood was one of renewed power.

Helen left them alone and Andreas sat down at the table, glanced at her without getting her to look back at him because she was staring out of the window, then gave a sigh. 'Are you going to brood all day? I thought we had exorcised some ghosts last night.'

'Did you?' She still refused to look at him. Did he think that all it took to exorcise the memory of Martine was a few hours in bed together?

'Those tears must have meant something,' he said flatly.

'Don't you know what they meant?' She turned then, white and angry, to glare at him. 'They meant that I was ashamed of myself.'

His face was hardening again, the eyes narrowing to dark points of steel which pierced her face. 'Ashamed of admitting you love me?'

It hit her like a punch in the stomach. She winced from the blow and his eyes watched her remorselessly.

'Oh, God, you bastard!' she groaned, covering her face with her hands.

'Is that why you couldn't bring yourself to marry

Colby?' He poured himself coffee and sipped it as though her answer were of no consequence to him, and she would have liked to empty the coffee pot over his head, but in a trial of strength, either physical or mental, she had no chance against him and they both knew it, so there was no point in risking violence which would certainly rebound on her own head.

'One marriage was enough for me,' she said bitterly.

'Yet you apparently intended to marry him.'

She shrugged. 'We were quite well suited. Why not?'

Andreas bared his teeth in a brutal smile. 'Colby would never suit you, my dear. He's too tame.'

That was so close to the truth that it entered her bloodstream like adrenalin, stirring her temper to hot rage. 'Don't sneer at Philip! You, of all people! You've no right. He's worth ten of you!'

Lazily Andreas put out a hand and curved it round her cheek. 'Yet you love me.'

She shoved his hand away violently. 'No!'

'Oh, yes, you do,' he said coolly. 'It hurt you too much to admit it. I wrung that admission out of you, Lauren.'

Her eyes were as wild as those of a mountain cat, bright green, filled with anger. 'But I don't want to love you.'

'I know,' he said, and now his face had a strangely sombre cast. 'You've made that very clear. I'm a despicable swine, and you hate my guts. Am I supposed to be flattered that all the same you can't stay out of my bed?'

Fingers curled to rake at his face, she flew at him

then, but he pulled her down on to his knees, fighting violently, and arched her back over his arm, beginning to kiss her. Then her stupid, treacherous body betrayed her again and her arms went round his neck, touching his hair, his nape, and she was groaning under his mouth.

At last he stopped and looked down into the hot, blind face bitterly. 'How could you let Colby touch you?' The words broke from him in a harsh accusation. 'Loving me like this, how could you, Lauren? Tell me now, did you go to him after you'd seen Martine in bed with me?'

Wearily she shook her head and Andreas winced. 'Before, then?' he asked thinly.

'He never has,' she said.

Andreas's hands bit into her shoulders. '*What?*'

'Oh, I was angry enough to sleep with the first man I met just for revenge,' she said in a tired voice. 'But I never did.'

He stared into her face, searching her eyes. 'Colby said. . . .'

'He lied,' she grimaced. 'We both lied. He's never been my lover.'

'God damn him,' he said hoarsely. 'The lying devil!' His whole face was white, a dead cold white without any sign of life except for the leaping hell of his black eyes.

'Andreas,' she said, disturbed.

He almost pushed her away from him, got up and walked from the room with his face averted and his body stiff. Lauren stood there, swaying, shivering, her mind in total confusion, because what had she said to make him so deeply angry? She had expected him to be amused, possibly triumphant, but not bitterly angry. That had not been feigned, that fierce explosion of rage. It had flamed out of him.

Was he just angry because Philip had lied? Surely he must see that Philip had been protecting her? She had been annoyed at first when she knew what Philip had told him, but then she had seen that it had all been done for her sake, to save her pride.

Why had Andreas been so furious?

CHAPTER EIGHT

SHE did not see him again for the rest of the day, nor did she go to him that night, her pride stung by the memory of him saying that she would come to him. Instead she sat in her own bedroom and looked through her sketches and saw things she had not known she had seen. It was not a new discovery. Her eye passed on to her hand impressions it had not given her brain except subconsciously. There was an elemental spareness about the island landscape which she found deeply moving. She knew she could paint here. She wanted to paint here. Her fingers itched, always a sure sign, her brain spawned images she knew she must capture on canvas.

She dreamt strongly that night, waking with a confused impression of conflict and pain.

The day was bright and clear, the sun quite strong for once, and the sea had a Mediterranean glitter, although far out on the horizon there were white-capped waves advancing towards the shore and the seabirds were close in to land, which often meant bad weather in store.

When she came downstairs Andreas was already there, reading his paper, his coffee cooling in his cup and a broken croissant bearing witness that he had eaten.

She halted, then drew a deep breath and came to-

146

wards him, and he looked at her over his newspaper. 'Sleep well?' he asked, and there was smooth mockery in his voice.

'Thank you. Did you?' She touched the coffee pot and found it lukewarm.

'Helen will bring some more,' he said, ringing for her.

Helen had anticipated the request. She put down the fresh coffee with a thud and looked at Andreas with arms akimbo. 'Have you told her?'

'Mind your own business,' Andreas said shortly, and Helen snorted, dark eyes furious.

'Isn't it my business? If you get worse who will look after you?'

'What are you talking about?' Lauren asked, looking at him with anxiety.

'Never mind,' he said, his mouth hard.

'The nurse,' said Helen, and Andreas lifted his black head and gave her a furious stare.

'Get back to your kitchen.'

'He's sending her away,' Helen went on, ignoring him.

'Get out!' Andreas roared, suddenly bull-like, his neck thick with angry muscle, his eyes flaming.

Helen went, tossing her head. 'If she goes, you'll regret it,' she said as she closed the door.

'You can't,' Lauren protested as soon as the door was closed. 'Andreas, don't be a fool!'

He picked up his newspaper and shook it, began to read again, his face unseen behind the pages.

'The only reason they let you come here was because you brought a nurse,' Lauren pointed out reasonably. 'Why send her away? What difference does it make?'

'She's a nuisance,' he bit out.

'Why? Because she makes you rest? Oh, Andreas, don't be so foolish. . . .'

'Because while she's here you won't stay with me all night,' he said, and Lauren found herself shaken rigid by that, she could not answer him at all.

He lowered his paper and his eyes held grim mockery. 'Now, will you?'

She looked away, blushing. 'That's no reason. . . .'

'Reason enough for me,' he said, watching her pink face. 'I want you in my bed when I wake up.'

She felt warmth in her whole body. There was tenderness in what he had said, a feeling quite different in kind from the fierce desire he had been showing her. There was something of the old teasing sweetness they had once had.

Huskily, she asked, 'When does she go?'

'Today,' he said.

'By boat?'

'Plane,' he said, and gave her a wry look. 'But don't make any little plans to stow away on it, *eros mou*, because you are staying right here. I want you with me all the time until the plane has taken off. That way I'll make certain you don't insinuate yourself aboard with some cunning little trick.'

'But if you haven't yet recovered fully how are we to know the signs?' she asked, frowning. 'I don't like it. Andreas, please. At least let her stay for a few days.'

'No,' he said with flat determination. 'She intrudes

too much. In any case, we don't need her. My mother is coming.'

'Lydia?' Lauren stared, surprised. 'When?'

'Today,' he told her, looking into her eyes. 'Does that please you?'

'You know I love your mother.'

He smiled and his eyes were gentle, reminding her of his mother's, filled with warmth. 'Yes, I know you do, and it always made me happy. She loves you, too, you know. More than Sybil, I often think. She and my mother never did get on too well. Sybil likes to throw her weight around too much. Mama's too gentle for such tactics.'

'Sybil never liked me,' said Lauren, frowning.

'No,' he admitted.

'She resented me because....' She broke off, embarrassed by what she had been about to say, suddenly remembering Sybil's hand on Niko's small shoulder, the possessive way she had turned the boy away from her.

'Because you were my wife,' Andreas finished for her grimly. 'Yes, I know. Sybil was always jealous even as a child. She would have liked to be a boy, the only son. She has a great thirst for power, for dominance. Her husband, poor fellow, has to bear it, but I've no intention of permitting Sybil to interfere in my life.'

Lauren had been about to say that Sybil resented her because if she bore Andreas sons they would be Keralides, heirs to the family inheritance, but she had no intention of saying so now. She merely nodded, agreeing with him.

Martine had given him the son he wanted. Lauren had always known that Andreas wanted sons. It was in his blood, the desire to fuel the future with male descendants. Sybil's resentment was understandable, after all; she had grown up knowing that as a female she was only an inferior product of the Keralides house. Giorgios had only cared about his sons, although he had preferred that they should marry into their own class and race rather than go outside it. He had planned to have Andreas marry Martine, had fostered a relationship between them.

'Your father hated me, too,' she said harshly, her body shaken with a sigh.

Andreas was silent for a moment. 'Yes,' he said at last, 'he hated you. I am sorry, *eros mou*. What can I say? He distrusted you because you were English.'

'He preferred Martine.' She had said it, although she hated having that name on her tongue, and her eyes held bitterness as she looked at Andreas.

His face was like a carved mask, no readable emotion visible. 'Yes,' he said coolly.

'And in the end so did you,' she said, getting up, needing to escape because the jealousy and pain were burning inside her again and she hated even to look at him.

'No,' he said, taking her wrist in an unbreakable hold.

She looked at him searchingly. 'What do you mean—no? What other reason could there be?'

Andreas was silent, his eyes hidden, and there was a shifting confusion in his expression, a hesitation, as though he wanted to speak but in the end couldn't, his mouth twisting bitterly.

'Don't play games with me, Andreas,' she whispered fiercely, pulling free, then she ran out of the room and found her jacket and went to walk along the cliffs, her eye automatically delighting in the bright glitter of the sea and sky even while her mind went on bitterly fighting against the enchantment he could throw over her senses.

Once she turned her head and saw his figure at the villa windows, knowing even at that distance that it was him by his black hair and the grace of his lean, hard body. He was watching her, reading her angry emotions by her body movements, and she felt angry that she should be so easy to read.

He hadn't apologised, explained, even regretted anything. He had taken her and she had thrown pride to the winds by telling him she loved him. He should be very satisfied now. He had won. Didn't he always?

The first mistake she made was in going to the hospital the first time. She should have told Lydia she was sorry but she could not go. In going, she had admitted her weakness for him, and he had seized on that. He knew how to use someone's strength in defeating them, and he had let her vanquish herself when he cunningly laid his trap. If she had really hated him that much she would never have gone, never taken off Philip's ring and assumed his again, never have kissed him, let him call her darling and love. Yes, she had made it easy for him. It was a bitter thing to admit.

She walked in the biting wind, under the cold Greek

sun, and had despair and self-contempt for companions.

She had to go back to the house in the end, of course. Where else could she go? Andreas met her at the door and stared into her face, reading all too easily the marks of her inward struggle.

'You look like death,' he said flatly.

'Thank you.' Lauren tilted her blonde head bitterly, her eyes hard and over-bright.

She felt like a defeated army, routed without hope, faced with the conqueror and hating while having no defence.

'You need a drink,' said Andreas, mouth compressed.

'That's an understatement,' she said, forcing a smile.

He gave her a strong whisky and she drank it, shuddering at the taste yet needing it. The colour crept back into her face afterwards, but her eyes still held the shame of the defeated, and Andreas saw it with a frown.

After lunch they sat together listening to music. Lauren felt strangely sleepy again and curled up like a dormouse beside him, her head drawn down by his hand on to his chest. She welcomed sleep almost avidly. It was one refuge which did not fail.

When she woke up she was still lying there but Andreas had gone, quietly pillowing her head on some cushions. The room was shadowy with late afternoon. Suddenly she heard the distant throb of the plane and got up. From the window she watched it circle and bank steeply before flying off into the blue-grey sky. The nurse had gone, then, and Lydia would be here any moment.

She must go upstairs and do something about her

ruffled hair, her crumpled clothes, before Lydia arrived. She was nervous at the prospect of seeing Lydia, afraid of what Andreas's mother would read from her face. Lydia knew her too well for her to be able to hide much, but she would, for pride's sake, make the effort.

She walked out into the hall and then the door opened and Andreas's voice drifted to her, speaking quickly in Greek. At the same instant Lydia came in, tiny and neat and weary-eyed. Seeing Lauren she smiled immediately, holding out her hands. 'My dear! Surprised to see us? Well, I am surprised to be here, but Andreas makes these swift decisions. What a journey! We ran into some electrical storms en route. I was afraid I would be sick, we were tossed up and down like netballs. But Niko enjoyed every second, thought it was all laid on for him. . . .'

Her voice died away as Lauren went white, her hand pressed against her heart as though it were contorted with agony.

'You didn't know,' Lydia whispered. 'Oh, Lauren!'

Then Andreas came through the door, the boy riding on his broad shoulder, laughing, his dark eyes so like his father's, his hands ruffling Andreas's hair.

'God damn you,' said Lauren, looking into Andreas's face with wild eyes, then she turned and ran up the stairs and shut herself into her room.

He came to the room later and knocked, called her name, but she wouldn't answer, couldn't answer. She was lying on her bed in a rigid attitude, her fist pressed against her mouth, the room darkening around her.

'Open this door,' he commanded sharply.

Somewhere the boy was laughing in the deep, delighted fashion of childhood, as though someone were teasing him. Lauren bit her knuckles, staring into the darkness.

'Do I have to break it down?' Andreas was not making an empty threat. His voice had a furious ring. 'You're behaving like a child, for God's sake!'

'Go away,' she said.

There was a moment's pause, as though the sound of her voice had surprised him, then he spoke in an altered tone, gently, coaxingly. 'I should have told you—I know. It was a shock to you, I knew it would be. I was afraid that if you knew you might try to go back on the plane.'

'Liar!' she accused. 'You would never have let me.'

'I'd have tried to stop you,' he accepted quietly. 'But with the nurse watching it would have caused trouble. I didn't want a scene with outside witnesses.'

'My father always said you were devious.'

'Open the door,' he said softly, his voice sounding close to the panels. 'It's absurd for us to talk through it. Do you want the whole house to hear us?'

'I don't give a damn,' she retorted. 'Let them hear. Why should I care?'

'It will upset my mother,' he said.

'Your mother? Lydia knows how I feel about the boy. Have you told her, or doesn't she need to be told, that I'm your mistress now, not your wife? That's the way you wanted it from the start, wasn't it, Andreas? I was never good enough to be one of the Keralides family. You would have seduced me without marrying me if you could, but I had a father who cared what happened to me, too much protection for you to dare to

take what you wanted without bothering to marry me.
It would have been so much more convenient for you
if I'd been fatherless.' She was shouting now, her voice
hoarse with pain and anger.

'Don't,' he muttered so low that she scarcely heard
him.

'Don't tell the truth? Why else did you bring me
here? You let me go easily enough before. You suddenly felt you wanted me again, did you, Andreas? And
this time there was to be no nonsense about a wedding.
You just reached out and took me. . . .' Her furious, bitter words stopped in a rush of blinding tears and she
buried her face in her hands.

'Open this door!' He smashed his fists against the
panels and the door shook. But it was too well made to
give beneath his blows and she didn't even lift her head.

'Go to hell,' she whispered thickly.

There was silence and she knew he had gone away.
She lay there watching the darkness thicken. The boy's
laughter had stopped. She wondered what Andreas was
doing, and knew she was behaving in a stupid fashion,
yet could not help herself. He should not have brought
the boy here.

Her anger was not so much because the boy reminded her of Martine. His resemblance to Andreas
outweighed that. But Niko's presence here now made
what was happening between her and Andreas seem
somehow degrading, a relationship which had no place
in his life. Niko was his son, a Keralides. She was just
Andreas's mistress, one of his women, used like them,
in time no doubt to be dismissed like them. Niko would
look at her and equate her with the other women he

had seen come and go in his father's life. That was what she found intolerable.

'In thirty seconds I shall shoot off this lock,' Andreas said suddenly through the door.

Lauren sat up on the bed, staring. He couldn't mean it. But he did, of course. He had a collection of beautiful weapons in his study downstairs and he knew how to use them. He was a first-class shot. It had once been his favourite hobby.

Sobbing, she opened the door, and he came in, pistol in hand, his dark eyes dangerous.

'You stupid little bitch,' he muttered, flinging the pistol on to a table. His hand forced up her chin, he flicked on the light and she flinched, dazzled by it. Andreas scrutinised her face, seeing the tears and lines of pain.

'You shouldn't have brought him here.'

'You can't ignore him for the rest of his life,' Andreas said. 'My mother said he was fretting for me. I'd shut him out since my accident and Niko was becoming disturbed by it.'

'You could have told me.'

'Asked you to let him come? What would you have said? You'd have insisted on leaving. Admit it.'

'As I insist now,' she snapped, facing him with her chin up and a feverish anger in her eyes.

He took her shoulders in his hands and looked at her, the dark eyes glittering. 'I'll never let you go again. You're mine.'

'You said that to my father, but we were divorced and you never came near me for five years.'

'Because I believed you had slept with Colby,' he

said, and she believed him, the depth of jealousy in his voice was convincing. 'I wanted to kill him, kill you, but you vanished and then I was told you were divorcing me. If I had found you I might well have done you an injury, so I let you go.'

'You still believe that it doesn't matter that you slept with Martine,' she said bitterly. 'It's always accusation with you, never defence. You refuse to see anything wrong in what you did, don't you, Andreas? All that matters to you is that a possession of yours went astray.'

One of his hands moved into her loose silvery hair, climbed up into it, winding strands of it round his fingers. 'It will never go astray again,' he said. 'I have you back, and I'm keeping you.'

Her eyes flared. 'You really think I'm going to be put in the position of being your mistress under the eyes of Martine's son?'

'Ah,' he said on a long-drawn-out note. 'So that's it.'

Her cheeks were burning. 'I won't put up with it!'

'Suppose we were married? Would that change things?' He watched her coolly, his face impassive.

Lauren drew in her breath. For a moment she said nothing, then she said huskily, 'You have never mentioned marriage before.'

'It seemed irrelevant,' he said, lips twisting.

'I can imagine,' she snapped, anger in her face. 'All you thought about was getting me into bed, wasn't it?'

He leaned towards her, smiling, tormenting amusement in his dark eyes. 'Nothing else. For weeks. Since I recovered my memory, *eros mou*.'

'You swine!'

Andreas's smile held mocking charm. 'What did you think about, Lauren? Tell me truthfully now.'

'Boiling you in oil, chiefly,' she said, but she was lying, and they both knew it.

'So, think now. If we were married, would you be able to accept Niko as my son?'

She looked away. 'Yes, I could accept him, but I'm not marrying you, Andreas, all the same.'

His hands tightened. 'Why not?'

She looked up with a harsh sigh. 'To be blunt, because I don't trust you.'

His face grew masklike, his eyes watchful. 'I see.'

'There've been too many other women in your life. I'm not going to walk in again some day and find another woman in our bed.'

'You won't,' he said flatly, and there was a grim look about his eyes and mouth.

'You may say that now, but you could change your mind. I believed you last time. You told me then that you would never want anyone but me, and I was young enough, and foolish enough, to believe every word you said. Jimmy and Philip warned me....'

His eyes flared with that bitter anger. 'Don't mention Colby to me, Lauren, or I am not going to be responsible for what I do.'

'You've never liked Philip!'

He gave a harsh crack of laughter. 'I hate his guts and he hates mine. We both knew that the day we met. We both knew why, too.'

Her face flushed delicately and she looked away, accepting that he was speaking the truth. Philip had always disliked him. She knew that. She had not understood Philip's immediate antagonism for a long time, but when she did have it forcibly made clear to her by Andreas she had felt sympathy and regret for Philip. He was an old friend, someone she trusted and felt affection for, and although she could not return his deeper emotions she had always been touched by them.

'He's always been very good to me,' she said quietly.

Andreas's mouth compressed. 'Of course he has,' he drawled coldly. 'He's a very patient fellow. He knew what he wanted and he was always prepared to wait in the hope of getting it.'

'I think you misjudge him,' she said, shaking her head.

'No, Lauren,' Andreas retorted. 'It is you who misjudges him.' He took her chin in one hand and looked into her face. 'But you will not marry him now. You will let me give him back his ring.' His eyes held a strange, hot glittering which puzzled and disturbed her. 'I shall take great pleasure in returning it to him, preferably shoving it down his throat.'

'Don't talk like that! It isn't fair to Philip! Whatever you feel about him, he's one of the nicest, kindest men I've ever met.'

The dark eyes narrowed on her face. 'He did us both a great wrong, Lauren. We owe him no favours, believe me.'

'What are you talking about?'

He shrugged. 'I told you. He lied to me, claimed you had slept with him that night.'

Lauren felt her cheeks stinging with heat and looked away, biting her lower lip. 'He did that for me. He knew how upset I had been when I saw you with Martine. He was only trying to save my face, salve my pride. I think Philip took it personally, he wanted to convince you I didn't care.'

'Oh, yes, he wanted to do that,' Andreas said bitterly. 'So he did it for you, did he? Do you really believe that? He did it for himself. He saw a chance and took it with both hands, the opportunity he had been waiting for, the chance to split us apart and get you for himself.'

She pulled away with a sudden return of that agonising pain. 'We would have parted anyway, after what I'd seen!'

Andreas stared at her coolly, shaking his head. 'No, Lauren.'

Hotly she cried, 'Yes! I may have been a little fool, too credulous to realise what sort of man you were, but even I couldn't have turned a blind eye to finding you in bed with Martine like that.'

'What you saw didn't part us,' he said in clipped tones. 'Colby did.'

Lauren felt despair then. Couldn't he see it? Couldn't he understand? Was he so blind to his own betrayal of her, to her pain, that he could honestly believe she would have agreed to ignore his infidelity?

'It's impossible,' she groaned, putting her hands to her face. 'We talk a different language, Andreas. I can't accept that a man has the right to break his marriage vows while a woman is expected to be faithful to them.' She lowered her hands, her face white now. 'It wouldn't work any more than it did then. Perhaps a Greek girl could shrug over a thing like that, but I can't. You have to understand that. I'm not talking about morals or the law, Andreas—I'm talking about love.'

'Love,' he said very softly, his hand sliding up her arm to her throat.

'Don't!' she said, pulling away. 'Oh, you can make me respond—I can't begin to deny that. But I'm not talking about sex, I'm talking about trust and honesty and I could give you neither, Andreas. Not any more. Do you think I want a marriage where I'm constantly wondering whose bed you're in? What sort of life would that give me? It would drive me crazy after a while.'

He looked at her expressionlessly for a moment, the strong sensual mouth tight, then he shrugged. 'Very well. Fix your face, brush your hair and come down before Lydia and Gregori think I've murdered you.'

'Gregori?' She stared, taken aback. 'What's he doing here? Why on earth did he come? Don't tell me Sybil's here, and Stephanos; has the whole damned family come? What's going on? Is it a gathering of the Keralides clan?'

He moved to the door and glanced back at her over his shoulder, his dark features enigmatic. 'I asked Gregori to come.'

A spark of malice lit in her for some reason she could not fathom. 'That was unwise of you, Andreas. It would have made Gregori curious. He always did fancy me.'

Andreas shot her a hard, narrowed look. 'Gregori flirts with every female he meets, my dear. He's a born opportunist.'

'You're not surprised to hear he flirted with me?'

He smiled wryly. 'I'd be surprised to hear he didn't.

You're very beautiful. It did not escape my attention that he had an eye on you.'

Lauren bristled at something in his voice. 'But you were so sure of me, weren't you, Andreas?'

He smiled oddly. 'I trusted you, my dear,' he said, leaving the room, and the reply made her tremble.

CHAPTER NINE

LAUREN took her time in getting ready, feeling too embarrassed by what had happened in the past hour to be eager to face Lydia and Gregori. It was half an hour before she left her room, walking slowly down the stairs and pausing in the hall to listen to the low murmur of voices from the salon. It was easy to distinguish Gregori's slow deep voice. Lydia was laughing softly. 'How silly,' she said as Lauren pushed open the door and stood there looking at them defiantly, head held high, her eyes over-bright.

'There you are, my dear,' Lydia said as calmly as though nothing had happened. She patted the place beside her on the sofa. 'Come and sit with me.'

Looking quickly around the room, Lauren saw that Niko was not present, and Lydia caught that look and understood it. In a quietly even voice she said, 'Niko is in bed.'

Lauren flushed. 'I see.' She crossed the room, conscious of Andreas's dark eyes on her slender body, travelling from the high swell of breast beneath the silk dress to the long, smooth legs beneath it. She sat down, crossing her legs, and her glance flicked to Gregori, whose amused gaze was fixed on her too, with an expression easy enough to read buried in his eyes. Lauren gave him a hard, provocative smile. 'Hallo, Gregori. What made you leave the fleshpots of London?'

'Andreas,' he replied smilingly. 'What else?'

'What else,' she agreed, not turning to look at Andreas.

'What will you have to drink?' Gregori asked her, rising to see to it.

'Martini,' she said, and he deftly poured one and brought it to her, the glide of his appreciative eyes moving over her again as he bent to put it in her hand.

'You've grown lovelier than ever in the time since I saw you last,' he said in that purring voice of his.

She looked up then down, lashes flicking flirtatiously, doing it deliberately, aware of Andreas watching them. 'Thank you, Gregori.'

'Have you been painting while you were here?' Lydia asked quickly, a note of anxiety in her voice.

Lauren turned to smile at her. 'I've done some sketching. This is a place I've always wanted to paint. When I get back to my studio I shall paint a large landscape, I think. I've got dozens of ideas.'

'Are you going back soon?' Gregori enquired, shooting a look at his cousin.

'No,' Andreas said unhurriedly, leaning back in his chair, the glass in his hand. He sipped his whisky and watched Lauren, who refused to glance in his direction.

'As soon as I can,' she said, as if he had not spoken. 'I must get back to work. I've wasted too much time as it is.'

'You're gaining quite a reputation,' Gregori commented, a different expression in his face. 'You must be beginning to make money at it now, Lauren. I read an article about you in an American magazine last time I was in the States.'

'Yes, Philip showed me it,' she said, smiling, and Gregori gave her a strange little smile, his eyes wandering over her in a fashion which she did not like.

'Ah,' he murmured softly, 'your fiancé. Does he know you're here, by the way?'

Andreas was looking into his glass, swirling the amber liquid round, his face enigmatic.

Lauren felt herself colour. 'Yes,' she said flatly, looking at Gregori defiantly, daring him to say another word about it.

'How broadminded of him,' Gregori drawled. 'If you were mine I fancy I'd be a little more possessive.'

'That's enough!' said Andreas with a snap of his teeth.

Gregori gave him a little sneering smile. 'Come, she's not your wife any longer, Andreas. And it seems she's free to choose her own partners, with or without Colby's consent.'

Andreas leaned back languidly, but his face was hard, his eyes murderous. 'Do you want me to kill you?' he asked almost wearily.

Gregori bared his white teeth like a dog, his expression barbed. 'Aren't you tired of her yet? You've had a week of her. I thought that might have been why you brought me all this way, Andreas, to take her off your hands. It wouldn't be the first time I've been thrown one of your discards, would it?'

Lauren felt humiliation burning in her face. She leapt to her feet and Andreas clamped a hand down over her wrist, thrusting her back into her chair as if she were a child. 'Stay there,' he said tersely.

'And listen to him?' she burst out with burning

hatred in her voice. 'What are you trying to do to me, Andreas? Is it why he's here? Am I to be handed over to him like a doll you're tired of?'

'A very pretty doll,' Gregori purred, a light in his eyes which sickened her. 'You may not find the exchange as unwelcome as you think, Lauren. I may surprise you.' He lingeringly examined her, bringing scarlet to her face from her neck upwards.

Andreas rose in a deceptively lazy movement. There was nothing lazy about his expression and Gregori backed suddenly, his face filled with panic. The strong hands shot round his throat. Gregori struggled vainly, writhing and coughing, his hands unable to break Andreas's grip. Then he was suddenly flung into a chair, gasping for breath, his face purpled with agony. He lay there, rasping, fingering his throat.

Andreas stared at him grimly. 'You're lucky to be breathing at all,' he muttered. 'I only let you go on because I wanted Lauren to see what sort of swine you are under that polite manner of yours.' He glanced at her. 'I let him think he need not treat you with particular care so that you would catch a glimpse of his real nature. You had to see that, but I'm sorry he hurt you, Lauren. It wasn't easy for me to listen to all that, either, believe me.'

Lydia leaned over and touched her arm, her face gentle. 'I want to tell you a story,' she said.

'I don't want to hear,' Lauren muttered. She got up and Andreas said tensely, 'You've got to listen. I brought them here so that you should hear this. If I'd told you, you wouldn't have believed me. Listen to my mother, Lauren.'

'Lydia has proved she'll lie if you want her to,' she retorted angrily.

'She isn't lying this time.'

'How do I know that? I'll never believe a word she says again.'

Andreas stared at her, then gave a hard glance at Gregori. 'Watch him. You'll believe it.'

She looked at Gregori and saw shock in his face. He was gazing at his cousin, his features revealingly disturbed, a hard coin of red on his cheekbones.

Slowly Lauren sat down. She looked at Lydia. 'Well?'

Lydia looked into her eyes. 'I don't need to tell you that for several years before Andreas met you, my husband had been trying to persuade him to marry Martine.'

Lauren bit her lip. 'No, you don't need to tell me that. Your husband made that very clear to me.'

Lydia sighed. 'Yes, Giorgios had an obsessive desire to see Andreas marry a Greek. He did not like the English very much. He also did not like the idea that his son had a mind of his own. He wanted to impose his will on Andreas, but Andreas had a will of steel. He was too much like my husband to bow down in front of another man's strength. They quarrelled bitterly about it—Giorgios was very open on the subject. Martine knew that she had been selected as my son's bride.' Lydia looked sidelong at Andreas, sighing. 'Unfortunately, Martine was very eager to take that place.'

Gregori spoke thickly, his throat still painful from his cousin's rough handling. 'The little bitch was infatuated with him.'

'That annoyed you, didn't it?' Andreas asked him coldly.

Gregori glared at him. 'It sickened me, watching her fawn on you as though you were some sort of god, while you gave her the cold shoulder. She should have had more pride.'

'As you would have done?' Andreas lifted a dark eyebrow.

'She let you walk all over her,' Gregori muttered. 'She thought you'd marry her in the end even though you seemed to dislike the idea. When you married an English girl, Martine was left high and dry, looking a fool. I'd warned her, but she wouldn't listen.'

'But you were ready to comfort her,' Andreas murmured softly.

Gregori's skin flushed deeply. He did not answer, staring at his cousin, eyes shrewd.

'You pursued her relentlessly,' Andreas said. 'A bombardment she found irresistible in the end. How long did it take you, Gregori? Six months? Nine? She wasn't easy, was she? You really had to work hard.'

Gregori sneered, his temper flaring out suddenly. 'Don't flatter yourself! She was ripe for picking after you'd humiliated her by marrying someone else. All her friends had been waiting for invitations to the wedding. What do you think she felt like? She fell into my hands like a ripe fig.'

Lauren stared at them, her mind working dazedly. So Martine had had an affair with Gregori? It did not surprise her, but she did not see what that had to do with what happened later.

'Is that how you are going to describe it to your

wife?' Andreas drawled icily.

Gregori took a hard, shaken breath and his high colour faded, leaving him livid. 'You can't!' He stared at Andreas with stricken eyes. 'You couldn't tell her, it would kill her.'

'You should have thought of that before,' Andreas said icily.

Gregori looked at Lydia, his face imploring. 'Lydia, you know what it would do to Rhea to hear about Martine! You can't let him tell her. She couldn't take the shock.'

Lydia had a sad, resigned look in her face. 'Poor Rhea, she deserved better than to yoke herself with a man like you.'

He winced. 'For God's sake, I'm a normal man, that's all. Do you think it's been easy living with a woman I love but can never touch? I know I knew the facts from the start, but I loved her too much to lose her. I wanted her for my wife, even though her heart meant she might die at any moment, and our marriage has worked, in its way. She knows I love her. She knows I've had affairs and she's turned a blind eye to them because in my position what else could she expect? But Martine ... that she wouldn't forgive. It would kill her.'

Lauren had forgotten it in five years, but now she remembered and was horrified. She had only met Gregori's wife Rhea once. Born with a congenital weakness of the heart, Rhea spent her life in bed, nursing her small store of strength. She lived quietly and rarely had visitors. But now Lauren remembered what she had known but forgotten. Rhea was Martine's sister.

Gregori's marriage had been one of convenience alone, she had imagined, knowing how rarely Rhea's name was ever mentioned, how much time the two of them spent apart. Gregori moved around the world in restless flight, but Rhea led that withdrawn, hermit-like existence in the country house which Gregori had bought for her. They had, of course, no children, and Gregori's private life had always seemed to exclude any interest in having any.

Lydia was looking at Gregori with contempt in her dark eyes. She shrugged her thin shoulders. 'You knew what you were doing,' she said. 'You seduced Rhea's sister quite deliberately, don't pretend you didn't. You knew it was the one betrayal Rhea would never, could never, forgive from you.'

He stared back at her like a cornered animal, his lips drawn back over his teeth in a snarl. 'Easy for you to talk,' he burst out. 'You can't imagine what it was like for me.'

Lydia shook her head. 'No? Rhea knew what you felt, she knew you were too highly sexed to put up with abstinence. She did not marry you lightly, Gregori. We talked of it for a long time before she gave you her answer. Rhea knew you wanted her for her share of the family money.'

'No!' he cried, and there was real pain in his voice now. 'She doesn't think that. She can't!'

'She weighed up all the consequences and the scales were heavy against you,' Lydia said quietly. 'But she loved you, so she decided to risk the pain she knew you would give her, just as she has bravely borne years of pain and fear from her condition.'

Abruptly Gregori dropped his face into his hands. There was silence for a few moments. Andreas lit a cigar and leaned back, smoking, his eyes on his cousin's bent head. Lydia looked undecided, watching Gregori. Lauren's presence was forgotten.

After a moment Gregori straightened, face white. 'I love Rhea,' he said harshly. 'That was why I wanted ... why I had to have ... Martine. She looked like Rhea.'

Lydia did not seem surprised by the confession; she nodded her head. 'Martine knew that. You hurt her, too, Gregori, making no effort to hide why you wanted her. You say her pride was hurt by Andreas, but at least he didn't use her to mimic lovemaking with her own sister.'

He got up and walked to the window. 'Why are you doing this? Why drag it all up five years later? Why wait all these years to threaten me with exposure?'

Andreas looked at the smouldering tip of his cigar, his face impassive. 'Niko,' he said.

Gregori swung, frowning. 'What about him?'

Andreas glanced at Lauren briefly, his face unreadable, then looked at Lydia in silence.

'Well?' Gregori asked impatiently.

Lydia said, 'Sit down, Gregori.'

'Oh, for God's sake!' he exploded.

'Sit down,' Andreas rapped out, and after a moment Gregori sat down and waited, his face angry.

'He is your son,' Lydia said softly.

Gregori sat up forcefully, staring at her, then looked at Andreas with narrowed biting eyes. 'Oh, no, you don't! You're lying. Do you think I never asked Martine that? My God, when I think. . . .' He turned his handsome face and a sneer crossed it as he looked at Lauren. 'I get it. You want to clear yourself with her, do you?'

'I'm not listening to any more of this,' Lauren said huskily, getting up. 'Lydia, I appreciate what you are doing, but for heaven's sake, don't lie about that poor little boy. I wouldn't want him hurt, Lydia. What sort of monster do you think I am?'

'I have proof,' Lydia said calmly.

Lauren stared and slowly sat down. Gregori looked staggered, his eyes dilating.

'What proof?' he asked hoarsely.

'Martine's own confession,' Lydia said gently, looking at him. 'I will show it to you in a moment. I still haven't told Lauren my story yet. Now be quiet, Gregori, while I tell her.' She looked at Lauren, the lines of her face forceful. 'The day you quarrelled with Andreas and went off to your father's house, Andreas had a terrible row with his father. He was in a disturbed state, Lauren. He got very drunk that evening. I found him in the chair in his study at midnight and I called two of the servants to put him to bed.' She grimaced. 'I am afraid Andreas was dead to the world. We couldn't wake him. The men put him to bed and left him there.' She sighed. 'Martine was in the house, of course. She knew what had happened. She came out of her room in a wrap and made some very unpleasant remarks about his condition, and the quarrel he had had with you. I was sharp with her, and she went off in a temper.'

Andreas interrupted deeply, 'I slept like one of the

dead all night. When I woke up I found Martine in my bed.'

Gregori laughed hoarsely. 'This is where the fairy story starts, Lauren.'

Andreas gave him a black look. 'Shut your mouth or I'll shut it for you!' He looked at Lauren. 'My head was pounding like a drum. I felt sick. The last thing I was in the mood for was a woman, particularly Martine. My God, Lauren, I could have had her any time I snapped my fingers.' He saw her wince and grimaced. 'I know, that sounds crude, but I'm afraid it's the truth. Martine practically offered herself to me on a plate many times. I just wasn't interested. I wasn't interested then—I told her to get out.' His face glittered with rage and pain. 'She laughed. Then she told me you had come back, walked in and found her in my bed. She'd seen you come in the front door, Lauren, and just for spite she had run into our room and climbed in bed with me. My God, the little bitch. You should have seen her face while she was telling me! She knew damned well what she'd done and she was getting quite a kick out of it.' He stared at her, the bones of his face sharp. 'I got dressed and rushed round to see you. I didn't expect to be met by Colby with a body-blow. He was lucky I didn't kill him. I wanted to, but he and your father together managed to kick me out of the house.'

Lydia took up the story as he paused. 'He came back to me in a terrible state. I was shocked by what he told me, but I was coming to see you myself. I knew you would tell me the truth and I told Andreas to leave you alone until I'd seen you. You know what happened.

You vanished and your father refused to pass on any messages. I told your father the truth about what had happened between Andreas and Martine, but he wouldn't listen.'

'You told my father?' Lauren was astonished, her face filled with disbelief. 'He never told me a word about it.'

'He never liked me,' Andreas said flatly. 'We both of us had fathers with views which made trouble between us, Lauren. Be honest. Your father would have liked to stop our marriage at the beginning and he did his share of seeing that it ended.'

'To be fair,' Lydia said softly, 'your father did not believe my story. He said it was too incredible. That may be why he did not tell you.'

'I wrote to you,' said Andreas. 'You never read the letters, did you?' His face had a hard glazed anguish. 'It wasn't easy for me, believing you'd let Colby love you, but I hoped it had been done as revenge, a balm to your own pride, just the reaction of someone who has been hurt. So I tried to reach you, but you refused and I couldn't find out where you were until you were divorcing me. I saw Colby then and he said you were marrying him.'

Lauren shook her head numbly. 'Philip said that?'

'He said you were in love with him and this time I believed him. I walked off wishing I could get my hands round your throat.'

'But you married Martine,' she whispered, staring at him.

He inclined his head. 'Ah, yes—Martine. It was all too obvious by then, you see, that she was pregnant, and when my father demanded to know the father, she said it was me.'

'So it was,' Gregori burst out. 'He's lying, Lauren. He's the father, I tell you. He had her that night.'

'No!' Lydia said sharply. 'Of course, Martine insisted that he was, and Giorgios demanded that as soon as Andreas was free again, he must marry her.'

'I was in a mood to care very little either way,' said Andreas. 'But I hated Martine for what she had done to us. It was all her fault and I told her so. She threatened to go to Rhea with the truth about herself and Gregori if I didn't marry her. That was when it all came out and when I guessed who the father of her child really was, and when I showed her I knew, she admitted it coolly. Oh, not in front of my father—she was too scared for that. We were alone.'

'How convenient,' sneered Gregori.

Andreas glanced at him. 'Except that I had taken a precaution,' he said quietly.

'What precaution?' Gregori asked, frowning.

'I tape-recorded every word,' Andreas said.

There was a silence and Gregori looked staggered, running his tongue over his lower lip as though it was suddenly dry.

'Once Martine knew I could prove she was lying to my father, she changed her tune. She became hysterical and said she would make Gregori recognise his child even if it killed her sister.'

'She meant it,' Lydia sighed. 'She was jealous of Rhea, she knew you had only wanted her because she was Rhea's sister and looked like her. I think she almost wanted to tell Rhea, almost welcomed the chance.'

'I couldn't let her do it,' Andreas said flatly. 'I'd lost Lauren anyway, so I married Martine and gave Niko my name. He was a Keralides, anyway, he had a right to the name.'

Gregori slowly rose. 'Even if Martine claimed it, there's no proof he's my child.'

'When he was born he had to have an immediate blood transfusion,' Andreas said in a quiet voice. 'You know why, I think, Gregori. You're Rhesus negative, aren't you?'

Gregori paled, staring. 'Yes,' he said thickly.

'And Martine's blood group was Rhesus positive. The child of parents with those blood groups is lucky to live and can only do so if his blood is changed immediately within minutes of birth.'

Gregori drew a long, unsteady breath. 'My God!'

Andreas shrugged. 'Martine didn't know, of course, nor did the doctors. They believed I was the father and my blood group was the same as hers. It was a shock to them when the boy was born blue.'

'Then he is my son,' Gregori said faintly. 'Good lord! Mine.' He looked hard at Andreas. 'Why have you never told me? You must have known I didn't know.'

Andreas looked blankly at him. 'You had no right. Even now, you've been denying him all along.'

'Because I didn't know,' Gregori rasped. 'If I had, do you think I'd have been anything but delighted? You know Rhea can never have a child. It has been unbearable for me to know I can never have a son. Now you tell me I have one, and one who carries Rhea's blood as well as mine.'

Lydia gave him a wry look. 'But you could never claim him,' she pointed out. 'Rhea must never know.'

Gregori looked stunned. 'I'd forgotten.' He closed his eyes. 'It's my punishment,' he said after a long moment. 'My son, and I can never admit it.' He walked to the door. 'It must be the Furies,' he said ironically as he went out. 'They get you in the end.'

When he had gone Lydia got up too and walked to the door, leaving Andreas leaning back in his chair, watching Lauren closely.

CHAPTER TEN

'WHY didn't you tell me all this long ago?' she asked him after a moment.

'You wouldn't have believed it,' he said softly. 'Even if you had listened, which I doubt. No, you had to have Gregori and Lydia here to make sure you heard the whole thing.'

Lauren looked at him through her lashes. 'You must admit, it sounds incredible.'

He grimaced. 'My father believed Martine, God knows. Of course, he wanted to believe her. He was delighted with the turn of events.'

She thought of Martine for the first time with compassion and understanding. 'Poor girl, she got hurt on all sides, didn't she? Between you, you and Gregori must have destroyed her.'

He gave a twisted little smile. 'If she got hurt, she used her claws in revenge, don't worry. She would have gone to Rhea, you know. She meant it. The fact that it would have killed her sister didn't mean a thing to her. She would use anything to get her own way. And she was determined to saddle me with Gregori's child.'

Lauren looked at him again, frowning. 'I suspect she loved you.'

He shook his head. 'Don't be sentimental, Lauren. Martine loved Martine.'

'Did you....' She broke off that question, lowering

her eyes, her face pink.

'Did I what?' Andreas asked drily, smiling.

She threw him a quick glance. 'You know what I was going to ask you.'

'Did I ever sleep with her?' There was mockery in his eyes. 'What do you think, *eros mou*?'

She gritted her teeth, wanting to hit him. 'How should I know? She was your wife for three years.'

He shook his head. 'She bore my name for three years. She never once lay in my bed, either with or without love. I didn't want her and I made no pretence of doing so. I made it plain from the start that ours was a marriage in name only. She got what she had wanted —she was my wife to the world. When she was drowned I couldn't even feel sorrow.'

'Poor Martine!' Lauren looked at the clock. 'It must be nearly time for dinner.'

Andreas laughed softly. 'Changing the subject? Now why, I wonder?'

She got up and he rose too, catching her arm, looking into her averted face.

'What's wrong now?' he asked teasingly. 'You do believe it, don't you, Lauren? I never touched Martine that night. I swear it to you.'

'I believe you,' she said sombrely. 'All the same....'

'All the same, what?'

She looked up into his hard face. 'Five years,' she said. 'Why did you wait five years to see me again?'

'Colby,' he said flatly. 'Now I did believe that. I could imagine only too well what frame of mind you would have been in, after walking in and seeing me with Martine. I knew Colby was just waiting for his chance. When he said you had given yourself to him, of course I believed him. I was as jealous as hell, but even then I could have forgiven that. You'd had a terrible shock. I thought if I could see you, we could wipe both things out, but you went away, and you divorced me. Then there was Martine and the coming baby. I had always been afraid of Colby's influence on you. I decided you preferred him and I made myself put you out of my mind.'

'Just like that?' she asked coldly.

He looked at her wryly. 'No, it wasn't easy, but I knew you were with Colby all the time. I assumed you were sleeping with him.'

'Weren't you surprised I didn't marry him?'

'Yes,' he admitted. 'But then I remembered the sort of life your father led and it occurred to me that you were following his example.' He glanced at her, eyes glinting. 'I'll admit I even hoped you were. It gave me satisfaction to imagine Colby trying to get you to marry him and failing. I was torn between hoping there were others in your life just so that Colby could suffer the agonies I'd suffered, and a grinding feeling of jealousy at the very idea that other men were touching you the way I wanted to touch you.'

Her skin bloomed with warmth and colour. 'What makes you think there weren't other men?'

He watched her, his mouth tight. 'Tell me there weren't.'

Her lashes stirred on her cheek, a teasing enjoyment in the curve of her mouth. 'Would you believe me?'

'I'd have to,' he said with a grating sound in his voice. 'Because God help me, I can't let you go again.'

Lauren looked up, trembling. 'I wanted to, but I couldn't,' she whispered. 'I meant to do it several times. I even took someone to my flat the night I heard you'd married Martine, but I just couldn't go through with it.'

'Who was it?' Andreas asked tautly, and she saw the jealousy in his eyes. 'Colby?'

She shook her head. 'I can't even remember his name. I met him and then I just forgot him. It never went beyond a few kisses, anyway.'

Andreas's mouth hardened. 'Just a few kisses,' he muttered deeply, angrily. He cupped her face in his hands and stared at her, his eyes darkly possessive. 'Never let another man touch you or I'll kill him. I love you. From the moment I saw you I loved you. You walked so gracefully, your hair looked like moonlight, and I knew I had to have you on sight.' He bent, groaning, and kissed her mouth. 'Lauren, tell me you love me.'

'I told you,' she said huskily.

'You hated admitting it.'

She sighed. 'Can you blame me? I despised myself for wanting you in spite of all that had happened.'

'And now?' He watched her with eagerness in his eyes, and she ran a finger over his strong, sensual mouth, feeling it quiver under her touch.

'Now I can say I love you without reserve,' she whispered.

He bent his head and their mouths met softly, tenderly, exchanging a kiss of quiet love, then Andreas slid his arms round her body, pulling her close to him, and kissed her with mounting passion, his lips hungry.

'When will you marry me again?' he asked her some time later.

'As soon as you like,' she said, leaning on him.

'There's one condition,' he said, touching her loose hair lightly.

She looked up, eyes wide. 'Condition?'

'Hmm,' he said, watching her. 'Colby. I want him out—right out. He did his best to keep us apart, Lauren. He is as much in love with you as I am. I don't want him anywhere near you in future.'

She frowned, sighing. 'I've known him all my life. He's done so much for me.'

'Too much,' Andreas said harshly. 'You can't have us both, Lauren. He has to go.'

She knew he was right. Regretfully, she nodded. 'Very well.' She gave him a wry smile. 'You won't refuse to let me see my father, I hope.'

'Your father's been my enemy, too,' Andreas said flatly, 'but I agree, I can't stop you seeing him, my love. All the same, he can come to us in future. You're not going to him. Colby would find that too tempting. Every time you went to see your father, he'd be there, and you know it. He and your father work hand in glove.'

Lauren put her hands on his broad shoulders, feeling the strength beneath her palms with a sensation of pleasure. 'And you, Andreas,' she said teasingly. 'I have a condition for you.'

'Oh?' His brows rose. 'What's that?'

'No other women,' she said. 'Or next time I won't run off to my father, I'll shoot you with one of your own pistols.'

He grinned lazily. 'There's one surefire way of making sure I'm never with another woman. Never leave my bed when I'm in it.' He kissed her throat softly, his lips warm against her skin. 'I want to wake up every morning and find you next to me, Lauren. That was the thing which drove me mad when I saw that picture in the papers and realised you were at last marrying Colby. I imagined the mornings when he would wake up and look at you lying next to him and I was almost out of my mind.'

'Tell me the truth,' she said, frowning. 'Did you crash because of that picture?'

He shrugged. 'God knows. I don't remember a thing about it. I was driving along thinking blackly about you and Colby, then the next thing I knew I was in the hospital. The doctors said my amnesia was a temporary side-effect of the operation on my brain. It wore off naturally. I think I began to remember the second time you visited me. You'd changed so much. I noticed it, of course, and things began to come back. I talked to my mother and she helped me to remember. It was then that I decided not to tell you I'd remembered. I wanted to go on seeing you and it was obvious you would stop coming once you knew I'd got my memory back.'

'It was typically unscrupulous of you,' she said without anger. 'Lydia should have known better than to agree to it.'

He smiled. 'My mother loves me,' he said. 'I was still pretty weak, remember. She didn't want to upset me while I was so ill.'

'What did you expect to gain by it?' she asked. 'You

knew I was engaged to Philip, that it was over between us.'

He glanced at her, his dark eyes amused. 'Over? Was it? I may have been weak, but my mind was still quite clear, Lauren, and every time I touched you I knew you were as aware of it as I was. Your face was very revealing. I supposed I secretly hoped I'd win you back from Colby, right at the start. Anyway, I meant to try, I wanted to get a little revenge, maybe, hit back at him.' He moved his hand slowly down her hair, ran it down her spine, so that she curved in against him languidly, her eyes filled with passion. 'And above all I had to see you. To touch you. I didn't dare go too far, but pretending I'd forgotten the divorce meant that I could kiss you when I liked, touch you and make you touch me.'

She looked at him with wry amusement. 'You really are a cunning, unscrupulous man, Andreas.'

'It was what kept me alive,' he said, quite soberly. 'It was a sort of fishing, keeping you dangling on my line, making you wriggle, watching you torn between escaping and giving in.'

'I could hate you,' she said, flushing.

'No, you couldn't,' he teased. 'You did struggle quite a bit and I watched every little attempt to get away. I knew you had begun to suspect, but by then I was determined to get you to the island with me. I was sure that if I had you alone I could....' He broke off and she eyed him ruefully.

'Could what?' she demanded suspiciously, already guessing what he had been about to say.

Andreas's eyes danced. 'Get you into bed,' he said,

and watched her face with amusement.

'You. . . .'

He silenced the angry words with a hand over her mouth. 'But I did, didn't I? With barely a fight.'

'There was a fight the first time,' she said indignantly.

He arched mocking brows. 'A preliminary skirmish,' he drawled with enjoyment. 'Which only added to the pleasure when you finally gave in.'

'I hate you,' she said, but she was laughing, and he pulled her close, his mouth burning down on her, demanding and getting a passionate response.

Later he said, 'What about Niko? Even though he isn't mine, I love the boy, Lauren. I've treated him as my son all his life. I can't just walk out on him now.'

'Of course not,' she said at once. 'Now I know he isn't your child I shall find it easy to love him. There'll be no jealousy in the way.'

'Our own children won't suffer,' said Andreas, winding a curl of her bright hair around his finger.

Lauren blushed. 'We'll face that when we come to it. But, Andreas, I think you should let Gregori see more of him. He's human. And was obviously shaken to learn Niko was his son.'

Andreas grimaced. 'So he should have been! He behaved quite abominably. He even made a pass at you, right in front of me, because he believed my accident had made me too weak to take him on. Gregori was always a jealous, malicious swine.'

'But he obviously loves his wife.'

'Rhea is a wonderful person,' Andreas said. 'Quite exceptional, and far too good for Gregori. But as Niko is her nephew, maybe he could stay with her now and then.'

Lauren smiled. 'That would be lovely.'

A rap on the door made them both start. 'Come in,' called Andreas, and Helen put her head into the room, eyeing them both blankly.

'Are you eating tonight or not?' she asked in Greek.

'What makes you think we're not?' Andreas asked blandly.

She snorted, her face sardonic.

'We're coming,' Andreas said then, grinning at her. 'So take yourself off and give me a chance to kiss my wife.'

'If you haven't done that yet you've been wasting the last half hour,' retorted Helen, whisking out of the room and banging the door.

'I've been wasting five years,' Andreas said grimly. 'I've a lot of catching up to do.' And he kissed Lauren deeply, his arms tight. 'I don't have to wait until our marriage, do I?' he asked huskily as he drew his head back.

'For what?' she asked, opening her eyes wide in sweet innocence.

'Witch,' he muttered, kissing her again, hard. 'We could be married in a week, but a week seems a very long time to me.'

'Fasting is good for the soul,' she said demurely, escaping from him and leaving the room.

Helen looked round as they came into the dining-room and gave them a sharp nod. 'Dinner is ruined—I hope you know that.'

Lydia smiled at Lauren. 'Take no notice, my dear. Helen does fuss so.'

'Huh!' snorted Helen, stamping out of the room. There was no sign of Gregori and they sat down to the perfectly cooked meal in a warmly relaxed family atmosphere, talking about the wedding, discussing the repercussions which might follow.

'The family will be up in arms,' said Lydia. 'It will cause a sensation in the press.'

'Not that much,' Andreas shrugged. 'I think it's known now that Lauren is here with me. People will be busy putting two and two together.'

'Not necessarily,' said Lauren, her eyes on her plate. 'I imagine they think my presence here is easily explained.'

Andreas leaned towards her, eyes teasing. 'Really?'

She gave him a dry smile. 'You know what they'll think.'

'What's that, light of my life?'

She gave him a furious look. 'Well, they don't think I've come here to marry you again, that's for sure.'

He smiled mockingly. 'And so soon after your engagement was announced. That must have stuck in Colby's gullet.'

'Oh, be quiet!' she snapped, infuriated. 'Poor Philip.'

'Which reminds me,' he murmured. 'Colby's engagement ring. Give it to me and I'll send it back to him.' A spark of malice lit his dark eyes. 'With a suitable note of explanation.'

'You won't,' she said. 'I'll do it myself. I can imagine what your note would say.'

'I owe him such a lot,' Andreas said softly, his face hard. 'I'd like a chance to tell him so.'

'Don't, Andreas,' begged Lauren, distressed. 'Just forget it.'

'Five years?' he asked harshly. 'You expect me just to wipe out that debt without a word?'

'It's over,' she said soberly, laying a hand over his on the table. 'Can't we start again, Andreas? Do you want the past to poison the future?'

His face changed. 'No,' he said, looking at her passionately. 'But, darling, I always get so bad-tempered when I'm fasting.'

Lydia looked at him in puzzled surprise. 'Fasting, Andreas? Surely you are not dieting when you have been so ill?'

Lauren was blushing under his wicked, amused eyes. 'You don't play fair, Andreas,' she protested.

Lydia gave a little gasp of understanding and stifled her smile, looking away.

Andreas held Lauren's gaze. 'Well? Do I fast or not?'

'Shameless blackmailer!' she groaned. 'Why do you always have to get your own way?'

He lifted her hand and kissed it with an upward glance of promise. 'That's the way I am,' he said to her softly.

 **The very finest in romantic fiction**

Get all the latest books before they're sold out!

As a Harlequin subscriber you actually receive your personal copies of the latest Presents novels immediately after they come off the press, so you're sure of getting all 6 each month.

Cancel your subscription whenever you wish!

You don't have to buy any minimum number of books. Whenever you decide to stop your subscription just let us know and we'll cancel all further shipments.

 *Sweet Revenge* by **Anne Mather**
Devil in a Silver Room by **Violet Winspear**
Gates of Steel by **Anne Hampson**
No Quarter Asked by **Janet Dailey**